# ERNESTO DESIDERIO

GW00671623

# FORMULA ONE
# RACE ENGINEERING

## OPTIMIZING A DRIVER'S
# PERFORMANCE
## WITH A WINNING METHOD

THE BOSS BOOKS

FORMULA ONE RACE ENGINEERING

Ernesto Desiderio

Design by The Boss Books Editions

One Hour Marketing Srl
via Alessandro Volta 34, 20825 Barlassina (MB)

www.thebossbooks.com

Printed in October 2021

ISBN 9791280622051

# CONTENTS

# CONTENTS

# CONTENTS

Nikita Mazepin, Bahrain Test 2021.
Courtesy of F1-Fansite.com

# FOREWORD *by Romain Grosjean*

I've been racing for more than 20 years and I'm very proud to have the opportunity to write this foreword for Ernesto's book.

Race cars are made of carbon, but they need chemistry with their driver to go fast. That's what makes all the difference. Engineers are the link between the human part and the mechanical part of motorsport. It sounds straightforward, but it's not simple at all.

First of all, you have to understand the physics and the dynamics of your race car, which is something that requires a lot of study as well as first-hand experience on the race track.

But you also have to relate well to your driver, focusing on his feelings and emotions. From my point of view, this is the most important aspect of the job. It's essential for an engineer to create a connection and establish the best possible relationship with his driver. Being able to understand the human side of racing and the psychological implications of driving under such pressure is a rare skill.

I have worked with many great engineers throughout my career, but the best ones are those who understand the driver and are able to give him the confidence he needs. Ernesto is one of them: he has given me invaluable support and helped me improve my performances on many occasions.

It's all about small details, but that's what makes you win or lose.

# INTRODUCTION

Monaco, 1989. The first time I laid eyes on a Formula 1 car live, I was a three-year-old boy sitting on his dad's shoulders. Although I felt that I had the best seat in the world, the view was quite limited from up there. Yet I could see all I needed to see: as I watched the cars coming out of the tunnel like rockets and braking for the Nouvelle Chicane, I decided that racing was going to be my life.

The emotion I felt when the noise of the cars rumbled through my body is unforgettable.

The reason why people love motorsport so much lies in the emotions that are generated on a race track. It's the old story of a man or woman and a race car – either you love it or you just see a bunch of cars going round and round at great speed for no apparent reason.

If you do love it, you will be captured by the magic of a unique world – and if you have the privilege of working in this industry, you soon realize you can't live without racing. I was hooked on day one.

Although most people watch races on television or a computer, some are so passionate about this sport that they prefer to go to the race track to watch them live from the grandstands and soak up the incredible atmosphere. If you are lucky enough to know someone who can provide you with a couple of passes, your experience will be even more memorable, because you'll be able to watch the race from the privileged perspective of the paddock.

The people who work in this business have a different, but no less exciting, point of view. As an insider, you live motor racing on your skin and your job becomes your mission. The glamor and the parties soon lose their shine to make way for a lifelong commitment. You acquire a separate family, the so-called "circus", and you end up spending a lot more days with them than with your own family. You dedicate your days to making your team faster by giving your driver the best car you can, so he can show his talent and repay your efforts with his results.

The driver is the central character in this world: being the human factor at the end of the chain, he is the focus of everybody's attention. Millions of eyes are turned toward him, as people admire his amazing ability to drive a car at the limit while racing his fellow drivers, who are all trying to get ahead of each other. There is no room for mistakes, cowardice or indecision.

Some drivers have an easier life, because the car they are driving is simply faster than the competition – which allows them to achieve better results and consequently higher rankings. Yet, even with a faster car, winning a race is not as easy as it may look.

Undeniably, it is uncommon for a driver to be faster than his competitors despite driving a less powerful car. This is an especially rare event in Formula 1, where sadly in the last decades we have witnessed the triumph of engineering over human talent. However, now and then we can still see amazing achievements that remind us all why we love this sport so much. When a driver outperforms competitors who are racing with better equipment and triumphs against all odds, it is an emotional experience for everybody.

Whenever this magic happens in a race – or even just a lap, a corner or a sector – it's never by chance. These things don't just happen: they are the result of a series of performance factors that have combined to make the whole package faster.

We all know that race cars are constantly being developed and improved in every possible way. Teams spend millions in cutting-edge technology and hire the best engineers and specialists to monitor and optimize their cars. A huge amount of data is gathered and analyzed to diagnose any possible problems and find the most advanced solutions.

Cars are only one part of the equation, though. If we want the whole package to be fast, we need the driver to perform. Differently from a car, a driver's performance cannot be improved by means of technology, as it's the result of an unmeasurable combination of perceptions, decisions and reactions that occur inside him when he is behind the wheel.

From the outside, a driver's life looks glamorous and exciting, but clearly this is just one of its facets. Becoming a professional race car driver requires a great deal of technical, physical and psychological preparation. Without discipline and mental toughness, even the most talented driver will be unable to handle the complexity and withstand the pressure of his job, especially in the top series.

After all, drivers are human beings who have to face the same type of fears and doubts we all have: Can I live up to my team's expectations? Can I be faster than last year? Can I be faster than the other drivers? Keeping anxiety at bay requires great mental focus and the kind of confidence that only constant training can give. It's not enough to give a driver a fast car – he also needs mental support and a clear, effective method to optimize his performance.

Helping a driver to up his game is one of the most difficult tasks for an engineer. However, precisely because of its difficulty and of the human element involved, it is also one of the most rewarding jobs you can possibly have. This has been my role for many years, and I have had the privilege of working with many professionals in the highest categories of motorsport.

Optimizing a process that is already close to perfection is not an easy task. How do you gain an edge over the competition in Formula 1 and the other top racing categories, which have the most technologically advanced cars and the most talented drivers in the world?

Throughout my career I have always strived to improve my approach by examining data, listening to drivers – who are the best sensors a car can have – and of course learning from my mistakes. As a result of this, I have developed my own method of optimizing a driver's performance – the P-D-R® (Perception-Decision-Reaction) Process – which breaks the driving process down into its main phases and analyzes which aspects should be worked on. The ultimate goal is to prepare the driver to deliver that extra tenth of a second that can make all the difference to the outcome of a race.

I've decided to write this book because I want to share this method with you and help you reach your objectives. This is what I wish I had known when I started working in this industry.

If you are a driver, this method will help you understand which areas you can work on to become faster and optimize your performance. If you are an engineer, it will help you identify the points you should focus on to improve your driver's performance and make your work more effective.

If you are a racing fan or a student who wants to work in this industry, you will find a behind the scenes account of the challenges faced by drivers both on and off the track – including several anecdotes from my years of experience as a performance engineer.

Finally, I'd like to add a remark on the subject of women drivers. Although you will find that I refer to male drivers throughout the book, I believe that gender is irrelevant – a driver is a driver! In my experience, it doesn't matter if there is a man or a woman behind the wheel, as long as the speed is there. Unfortunately, as we all know, nowadays the world of motorsport is predominantly male, and not only in the cockpit: when it comes to motorsport, there are still not enough women in the whole business. In the past decade there has been a significant increase in the number of women drivers (though less so in the top series) and things are slowly changing. However, there is still a long way to go and this is a loss for motorsport – women drivers have a lot to offer and I'm sure our industry will benefit from their contribution in the future.

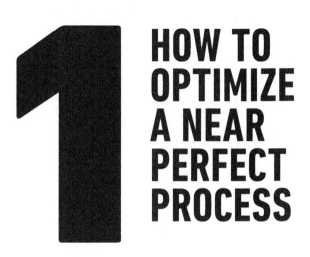

# 1 HOW TO OPTIMIZE A NEAR PERFECT PROCESS

Car number 24 in the pits, 2020.
Ph. by Andrew Roberts.
Courtesy of Unsplash Photo Community

IT MAY SEEM IMPOSSIBLE
TO FIND AN EFFECTIVE WAY TO
IMPROVE WHAT IS ALREADY
SO FLAWLESS, BUT IT'S
IMPORTANT TO REMEMBER
THAT THERE IS ALWAYS A
MARGIN FOR IMPROVEMENT.
IT'S BOUND TO BE SMALL
AND HARD TO IDENTIFY, BUT
IT'S THERE.

## The World of a Race Car Driver

Driving a piece of engineering art around a race track, challenging the laws of physics, is a difficult job, but also a privilege. Many young people are fascinated by this world and dream of being part of it. What fans and spectators may not appreciate is that the races they watch on television are just a part of a driver's job. They are the tip of the iceberg, the culmination of a long and complex process of physical and psychological preparation. This applies to all race car drivers, of course, not only to famous drivers in major series like Formula 1, IndyCar, NASCAR, World Endurance Championship and Formula E. However, the latter have an even higher burden to bear because of the intense public pressure they are subject to. As we all know, there are huge amounts of money at stake in every race, and drivers are always the center of attention.

Their lives are full of engagements, which sometimes distract them from the upcoming race: they need to keep in touch with the media, talk to their sponsors, make public appearances, negotiate contracts and so on. The fans look up to the driver – he is their hero, and he knows that he needs them as much as they need him. Marketing has a crucial role in motorsport and everything we do is related to advertising. After all, the whole industry depends on sponsorship money and drivers need to play an active role from this point of view as well.

As the media have gradually become more and more important to our industry, the tools we use to communicate with our audience have changed rapidly and continue to evolve. Nowadays we use

Instagram, Facebook and Twitter, but tomorrow there will certainly be other networks for the same purpose: communicating with the fans and updating them on your activities, ideas and initiatives. This is positive and useful for a driver's career, because it adds another dimension to his public image, although different drivers have different approaches to social media.

We just need to go back ten or fifteen years to see a very different situation. The only media covering the races were newspapers and television and consequently their audience was not as large. Another significant difference was the slower pace of communication, in contrast to today's constant feed of news. The more we go back in time the less complicated the drivers' subsidiary activities were.

Today drivers need communication managers to help them manage their media accounts and create the most appropriate communication strategy to enhance the team's public image. It has become so important to make the correct statement, put the right message out there and advertise in the best possible way, that sadly there is very little room for spontaneity. And yet, now and then, we see a driver having a complete meltdown in the heat of the moment. And guess what? That's just what makes him more popular with his fans. People love seeing the human side of a driver and sympathize with him when he shows his emotions, because they realize that he's just like one of them. When something like this happens, the press will always cover it extensively, because a heated comment is the exception to the rule, a drop of reality in a dry and sterile ocean of press statements. In case you're wondering, it must be said that at times we do observe authentic reactions in front of a camera, without the input of a mastermind telling the driver what to say and what to do. Unfortunately, they are quite rare occurrences!

When they are not driving, drivers are involved in various types of activities, which can be grouped into two main categories:

- Subsidiary Activities
- Technical Activities.

The first category encompasses all those activities I have mentioned above – tasks that are not directly related to racing, although they are important to the driver and the industry in general, because they have an impact on his and his team's image. There are some psychological aspects of the driver's preparation that are related to dealing with public opinion, which is a topic we are going to touch on later in the book. What other people think is important and can have an impact on a driver's performance.

The second group involves all those activities that are directly linked to the main purpose of the driver's job: racing.

Some of the main technical activities the driver is involved in are:

- Car setup and setup directions
- Run plan and test items
- Race strategies

- Tire and fuel management strategies
- Power unit strategies.

As for other activities, a lot depends on the category the driver is involved in.

As you can imagine, this aspect of the drivers' job has also become more and more complicated, as a natural consequence of the increasing technological complexity of the cars they drive. Formula 1 and LMP1-H cars, in particular, are conceptually so complicated that a team of engineers is needed to look after the correct operation of all their subsystems and make sure the cars run smoothly and reliably around the track.

**While driving the car at the limit around other cars, a driver may be asked to activate one of the 300-350 different possible settings through the steering wheel.** The steering wheels we see on camera, or live in the cockpit, have something like 30 buttons. A few of them are on/off functions, while others are rotary selectors and allow the driver to quickly change maps, like Brake Balance, Brake Shapes, Engine Braking, Throttle Pedal Maps – and each of these can have 12 positions.

There are usually also a couple of multi-selection rotary switches for the least likely adjustments: the ones that are rarely needed, but can make the difference between finishing the race or parking the car on the grass. To give you an idea of their complexity, each multi-selection switch can have up to 12 or 15 positions, and for each one of these there are 10 sub-settings that the driver can activate with buttons located behind the steering wheel.

A typical call from the race engineer would sound like: "Multi Alpha 8 - Position 11", which means that the driver should first reach the Alpha rotary position number 8, and then select the position requested with 11 clicks on another button.

If it's a call related to reliability and the driver mistakenly stops at position 10, his engineer will call him again on the radio to ask him to correct the position as soon as possible. In the meantime, the driver might need to change his normal Brake Balance settings through the corner, adjust the Engine Brake and the Differential, and manually deploy some Electric Energy to get rid of traffic.

The difficulty is not only due to the complexity of the car – there is also a huge amount of data, acquired through the logging system and the sensors, that is supposed to help us understand the status of each component of the car. This gives the engineers and the driver a lot of extra work, because they need to study the problem and try to solve it together. Understanding the data is not a given, though, since it's a very complex process that requires a lot of effort and experience.

With the introduction of electric motors a few years ago – and not just in Formula E – there is an additional variable to an already complicated problem: energy management. This is a fundamental aspect for cars with a hybrid system, like LMP1 or Formula 1, and even more so in Formula E. This is something that a young driver coming up to the big series has never experienced before. It's an additional variable that requires an extra mental effort from the driver, who is already engaged in managing all the other elements – the tires, the brakes, the engine, traffic and so on.

Although the cars involved in the IndyCar or NASCAR series are doubtlessly simpler machines than Formula 1 cars, drivers still have to master a very large set of parameters. I have learned from experience that preparing a car for an Oval Race is very difficult.

First of all, the operating window of the car is reduced compared to a road course. One could think that this makes things easier, but it's actually quite the opposite, because every parameter the driver can influence, from setup to driving style, has a higher relative lap-time sensitivity. Consequently, every decision becomes inevitably harder.

This is especially true when drivers race a few inches from a wall, going down into Turn One at over 230 mph at the most famous oval in the world: Indianapolis. All the IndyCar drivers I've had the pleasure to work with share the same feeling when approaching Turn One at 230 mph with the crowd on the stands: it looks so unbelievably narrow!

It's worth mentioning all of this to emphasize that nowadays driving at top levels is a far cry from operating some pedals and a steering wheel. It has become so much more than driving a fast car around a track! **Good drivers are endowed with talent and instinct, but** this is certainly not enough to handle such complexity. In order to perform well, drivers must have a deep understanding of the car as a whole.

## The Perception – Decision – Reaction® Process

As a performance engineer, I work with drivers to help them optimize their performance and achieve their best possible result. But how can this be done in the context of a near perfect process like Formula 1 racing? **It may seem impossible to find an effective way to improve what is already so flawless, but it's important to remember that there is always a margin for improvement. It's bound to be small and hard to identify, but it's there.**

**After working for many years with a variety of drivers and cars in different series, I have developed a behavioral model aimed at exploring and perfecting the driving process: the Perception-Decision-Reaction (P-D-R®) process.**

The engineering approach to a complex problem is to break it down into smaller ones. If we split the driving process into simpler phases, we can analyze each one of them to make it better and improve the overall performance.

This model breaks down the driver's activity into three main phases:

1. The **perception** of what is happening in the car and the options to consider;

**2.** Once this is clear, the driver needs to make a **decision** on what to do;

**3.** Finally, the decision made needs to be implemented, via a calculated or instinctive **reaction**.

The driver faces lots of different scenarios in the car, receiving radio calls to perform a switch change, drive differently to save tires, hold position or charge the car in front and pass as soon as possible, provide a balance feedback, choose between Dry, Inter or Slicks, and so on.

Each scenario will prompt a different response, depending on the driver's preparation and psychological condition. However, any response will include these three main steps: his perception of the situation, the decision he is going to make and his reaction.

If the process that leads to a specific action is healthy and correct in all its parts, all these choices offer opportunities to gain precious time.

History and experience show us that if our preparation and our decisional process aren't based on solid foundations, our efforts are likely to fail. **When we think about the time constraints involved in driving a race car – the fact that drivers have to make so many split-second decisions – we realize that a solid preparation is crucially important.**

**The P-D-R® model suggests that the driver's effectiveness is based on how well he performs in every single phase, which**

**will contribute to the successful execution of the whole process.** Each phase can be subdivided into sub-phases that require different key skills, which can be separately trained to achieve an overall improvement.

A driver's psychological condition comes into play in different parts of the P-D-R® process. Motorsport has always been such a macho sport that many drivers don't want to talk about psychology, because they see it as a sign of weakness. The truth is that an athlete's performance depends heavily on his psychological skills, which are a necessary basis for a healthy Perception, Decision and Reaction process.

Splitting the driver's performance into three phases gives us a way to discretize a process that is not discrete by nature. It's an oversimplification, but it allows us to come to grips with a complex problem. Let's not forget that science is full of oversimplified theories that have contributed to enhancing our understanding of the bigger picture.

In the next chapters we will elaborate the three phases of the Perception-Decision-Reaction® process, focusing on the key areas we can develop both from a technical and a psychological perspective. A professional race driver aims to improve each single area, knowing that it will enhance his overall performance.

Figure 1.1 shows a schematic representation of the P-D-R® process as we imagine it: a continuous, circular, closed loop process. The closed loop representation is due to the continuous nature of driving. The results of the driver's last reaction will have an impact on the car or the scenario, which will lead to another cycle of perception, decision and reaction – and so on until the end of the race.

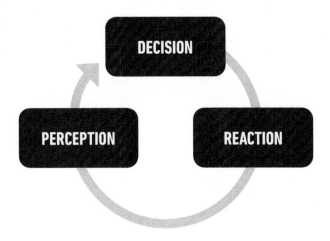

*Figure 1.1: P-D-R® phases and interaction*

There are two paths (both in a closed loop) that a driver can follow. The blue arrow represents the so-called **Standard** model, while the Red one refers to the **Instinctive** process.

The Standard path follows the three main phases, with each phase requiring a fixed amount of time. We will define as Standard every process that can afford to happen in more than one second. The choice of one second is an arbitrary one to cap the slowest possible reaction time of the driver. Conversely, everything that happens in a time that is comparable to the driver's reaction time will concern the red arrow shortcut.

The red arrow that connects Perception and Reaction can be defined as the Instinctive process, which describes a situation where the time between Perception and Reaction is so short that there is no time for a calculated Decision. During the Instinctive process the decision and the reaction take place directly in the Perception phase, in that subconscious database that contains all the information the driver has stored over years of training, learning and driving.

We'll see that the driving process is actually made of the simultaneous combination of the Standard and Instinctive processes. To use an engineering analogy, we could represent the Standard process as a low-frequency signal, and the Instinctive process as the superposed high-frequency one.

# KEY POINTS

- Driving motorsport series cars has become a very complex activity because of the increasing technological complexity of today's race cars.

- The driver's performance is still at the center of the sport and the team's performance depends on him.

- In order to improve the driver's performance, I have introduced the Performance-Decision-Reaction® model, a description of the driving process that allows us to discretize the single phases and the multiple skills involved in driving a race car.

- Breaking down the whole process gives us a method to better understand a complex problem, as well as many different ways and angles to improve it.

- The separate analysis of each phase will help us highlight the key points to improve, so as to achieve a global improvement of the driver's performance.

# 2 THE PERCEPTION PHASE

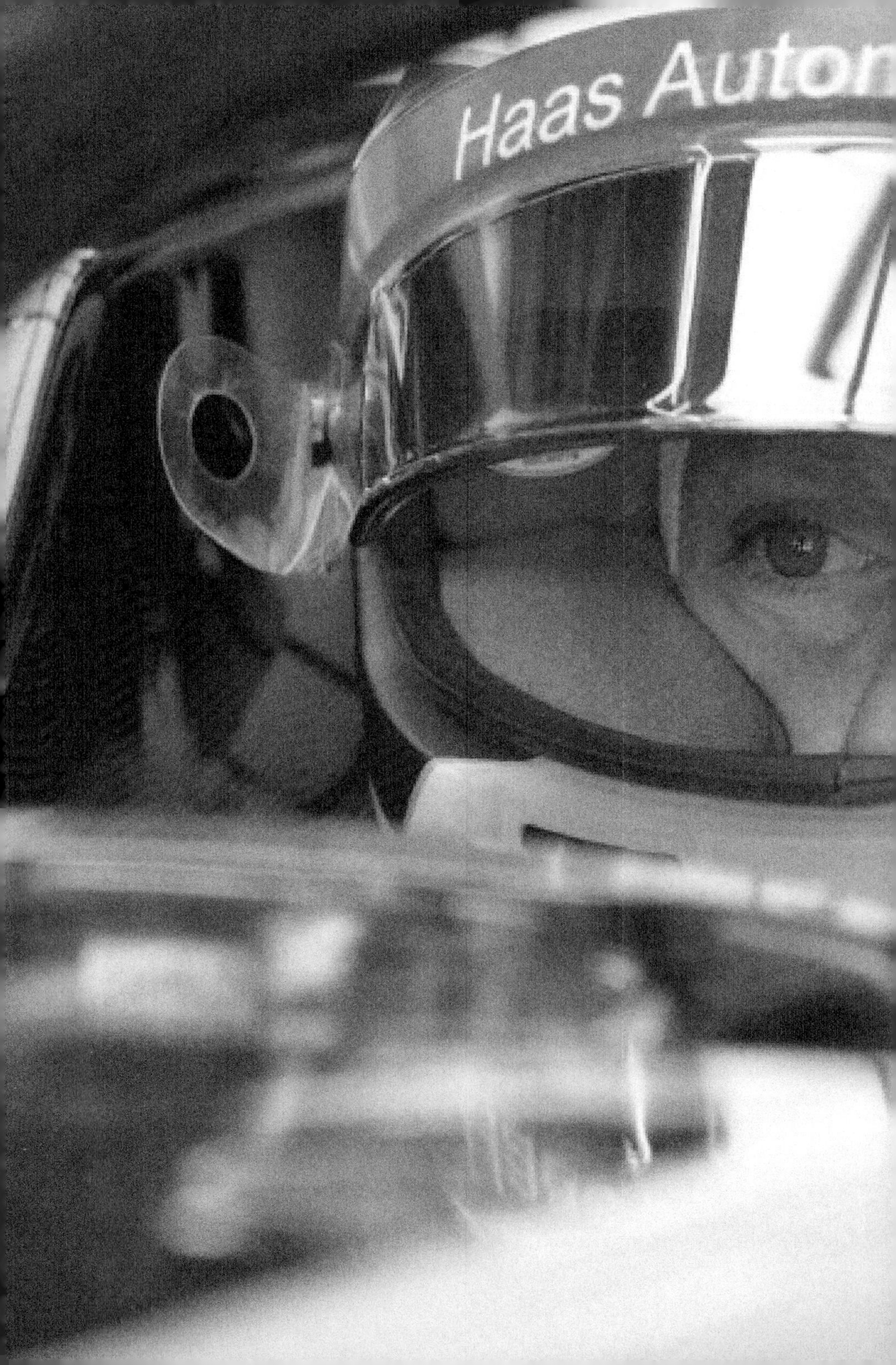
Haas Auton

Romain Grosjean.
Ph. By Andy Hone

ONCE A DRIVER FINDS THE KEY TO THE MENTAL ZONE THAT ALLOWS HIM TO MASTER THE UNEXPECTED, HE CAN UNLOCK AND EXPLOIT HIS POTENTIAL TO THE FULL.

The common view of a driver's perception skills is usually limited to his instinctive evaluation of car balance while driving. It is pretty naive, however, to think that anybody can drive a race car by just using his perception and his natural talent, especially when we take into account the degree of complexity reached by top-level motorsport.

Talent is part of it, no doubt, but it is only one of the elements required, even in the case of a young ace driving a go-kart. My experience on many race tracks around the world, working with the drivers, discussing setups and reviewing their performances, has taught me that pure talent is not enough.

Working closely with race drivers has made me realize that they need to understand most of the car's systems to be able to drive it on the edge. As I mentioned before, this is a consequence of the technological evolution of race cars as well as the ever-increasing competitiveness of championships at all levels.

Although there are many aspects of the driver's preparation that affect the Perception phase, I'd like to highlight four main areas that the driver can work on to enhance his performance. Each of these areas is not independent from the others – the overall Perception performance will depend on their synergy.

We can divide the first phase of the Perception-Decision-Reaction® process into four key areas:

- Balance evaluation

- The car performance envelope and controls

- The evaluation of external factors

- The athlete's psychological preparation

We are going to examine each area singularly to highlight the key points that allow the driver to understand where he needs to concentrate his efforts.

I have included the athlete's psychological preparation in the Perception phase, but it's important to keep in mind that this requirement applies to all three phases of the P-D-R® process. A solid mental condition is a factor that comes into play in each phase and, as we will see, it is essential for the driver to express his potential.

## Balance Evaluation

It's fascinating to consider the range of feedback that drivers give on their car balance perception: sometimes their comments can be deep and detailed, while other times they are simply along the lines of "understeer" or "tight", "oversteer" or "loose" here and there.

If the driver just complains about general understeer or oversteer when he comes back to the garage or speaks on the radio, there are usually two possibilities: either the car has a general problem and is far off its optimal setup, or the driver is just focusing on the biggest problem he can clearly perceive – and this is when it gets tricky for the engineers. For example, we can fix understeer or oversteer in many ways, but to do it properly we need to know where it is – in entry, mid-corner or exit, at low or high speed, on throttle, off throttle, and so on.

This to say that **details are fundamental in racing, at every level. The driver needs to focus on the car's behavior, trying to frame his feedback properly along the track, using his background preparation and specific reference points. His ability to provide appropriate feedback can make a huge difference for the engineers working on the car.**

Every little piece of information can be useful – and this applies to Formula 1, NASCAR, LMP1, IndyCar, Formula E and junior series. The amount of data is huge, and there is never enough time to go through everything. The bigger teams are able to assign specific tasks to different members of their staff in order to cover more areas, but not every team can afford to employ so many people. Anyway, it must be said that having hundreds of people looking at a problem does not guarantee that a solution will be found. This has been my experience with the American Haas Formula 1 Team: sometimes, even if you have lots of data and several experienced people looking at a problem, it might take a while to figure out what needs to be done.

Our 2019 car, the VF19, was fast in qualifying but not in the races, when it incurred in so many different balance issues that the drivers felt they couldn't do any better. We studied the data relentlessly, but we couldn't really pinpoint where the problem was. We looked at tires, mechanical setup, aero data and correlation, but nothing stood out: the data didn't provide any clear indication. Both our drivers, Romain Grosjean and Kevin Magnussen, felt very early in the year that something was not completely right.

It all started to become clearer when our drivers managed to tell us specifically what they felt and where. Romain pointed his finger down, highlighting the car's behavior in some parts of the circuit where the problem was more evident, and described what he perceived in greater detail. This allowed us to narrow down our search and gradually gain a better understanding of the issue.

We could have spent a much longer time looking for an answer if our drivers hadn't given us such a detailed description of what they perceived. This is an incredible advantage that drivers can give their teams, because weeks saved in understanding a problem will turn into weeks focused on studying how to solve it. As a result, the solution will be found sooner and the car will perform better earlier in the season.

A driver needs to be extremely aware of the importance of balance evaluation and of the implications of his feedback. His ability to convey his perceptions as clearly as possible to the engineers is crucial.

The more he drives a car and becomes familiar with it, the better he gets at understanding how that specific car feels. His memory is filled with tons of historical data – all the perceptions and the experiences collected during his racing career. A driver's accumulated experience can be seen as the sum of the raw data he has stored in his brain over time.

Let's imagine a driver, James, who has driven several race cars over 10 years, accumulating a total of 10,000 laps without any detailed discussion of the results achieved through all his work, without ever reviewing the data or reflecting on what he has been doing all this time.

Now imagine another driver, Niki, who has driven the same number of laps over 10 years, but with a radically different approach. After every race Niki would do the following:

- discuss it with the engineers
- look at the data
- review what he had done, trying to understand what he could have done better and what every change in the setup had given him in terms of performance
- discuss criticisms and suggestions
- take notes and write a clear review of what had happened over the weekend.

The raw data the two drivers have stored in their brains, linked to the total number of laps they have driven, will be the same, but the value of the information that Niki has collected will be infinitely higher than James's. This is because Niki will be able to link his physical perceptions to what the car is doing, thus enhancing his judgment and identifying the part of the car that is responsible for a specific sensation.

Using this approach will also help the engineers to gain a better understanding of the car's performance. As an engineer, I know how important this is not only for myself, but for the driver too. If I am aware of something that can slow him down, I will do all I can to avoid it, whether it's a specific radio call that annoys him or a setup that I know will limit his driving. The driver will ultimately benefit from the detail and accuracy of his feedback, because this will enable the engineers to provide him with a car he can drive faster.

In addition to this, by reviewing onboard video recordings and telemetry data we can pick up on lots of details, which can then be corrected. Cutting-edge technology enables us to do so many different kinds of analyses that sometimes it's difficult to decide what to look at.

Telling a driver what to do to improve his driving is not an easy task under any circumstances, but it is surprisingly harder with young drivers than with experienced ones. If you pick the wrong words or the wrong moment, you risk upsetting him or even spoiling your relationship. That's why emotional intelligence is an important asset for a driver: if he wants to improve his performance, he needs to encourage the people around him – who have a lot to offer thanks to their knowledge and experience – to feel free to provide constructive criticism and give him any advice they feel could help him. If his engineers get the driver's full attention and know that their comments won't backfire, there will be a positive outcome for everybody.

There is nothing worst for an engineer than to be told by a driver that he is wrong in front of other people, even if the issue being discussed is unimportant. A small incident like that will undermine the engineer's self-confidence, with the result that the next time he has a suggestion to make, he may not say anything to avoid provoking a negative reaction. Clearly this is not in the driver's interest, so friction with the engineers should be avoided as much as possible. It may happen in the heat of the moment, but then the air needs to be cleared as soon as possible.

It must be said that the engineers' suggestions are not always useful. I can say from experience that it's not easy to provide helpful advice just by looking at data and videos. If the driver thinks that a suggestion could be interesting, he usually tries it out on the track. Then, when he's back in the garage, it is always a good idea to discuss it with the crew to see if it was effective. However, if the advice doesn't seem to be useful, the driver shouldn't just ignore it – it's much more productive to explain why he thinks it won't help. This kind of approach will achieve one of two possible results: it will either persuade the engineers that it's not the best way to proceed, so they won't waste any more time looking into it, or it may help the driver get a better understanding of the advice and persuade him that it's worth trying it out. In any case, it's always better to talk about it, because in my experience it saves time and prevents any possible misunderstandings.

Taking notes and writing a review of the weekends is helpful at any level, from Formula 1 downwards. I would expect a driver to note down different kinds of information at different stages in his career. In the early stages he could be more interested in driving lines and braking marks, as well as the special features of a race track. Once he has acquired more experience and is more familiar with the race tracks and the marks, a professional race driver will focus on what went well over the weekend, what changes to the car worked and what he could have done better.

Engineers write reports too, of course. One of the tasks of a performance or race engineer is to review the race weekend and produce a report that includes comments on that specific track (which will be useful the following year) and on more general aspects of the weekend (which can also apply to the next race, wherever it may be). It's not just a matter of reporting events, issues and observations – we also draw conclusions on the topics analyzed and highlight the key points that we believe can be of use to the team in the future.

After writing my review, I present it to my colleagues, so I have to be precise and accurate and make sure that everything makes perfect sense, in case I need to defend my conclusions. Drivers don't have to share their notes with the team – it's understandable that certain notes are for private use only – but it's important for them to be aware of the implications of events and to write them down for future use.

The whole reporting process is extremely important, not only because it serves the purpose of keeping a record of events, but also because it helps the writer get a clearer mental picture. **Reviewing what you have done with a critical eye is always very helpful, because it triggers a self-correcting process that goes deep into the folds of your subconscious memory. The next time you find yourself in a similar situation, you'll make use of those insights. It's a very powerful tool.**

## The Car Performance Envelope and Controls

*Tim: "Harry, he doesn't need to appreciate your job to do his."*

*Harry: "He sure as hell does 'cause how can he expect to race if he doesn't know what a race car can and can't do?"*

Like many other people in this business, I grew up watching movies like *Days of Thunder* (1991), the story of a driver who has just entered the world of stock cars and is trying to adjust to an environment that is very different from anything he has known before. If you haven't seen it yet and you're a motorsport fan, then it's about time you turned your TV on and watched it. It's a great movie!

The lines above are from a scene in which the team owner, Tim, is discussing the ability of his new driver with Harry, the crew chief. It's a bit romanticized, but it helps to make a good point. A driver is expected to know what his car can and can't do, what he can ask her to do and what he should avoid. I'm not only referring to the grip limits in a corner, but to all the information that allows the driver to understand what limits the performance of his car and to know when he can push a button to make it faster or change a setting to help the balance.

**Our subconscious is heavily involved in the act of driving, especially in the instinctive process domain. Being well informed on the general car performance envelope will raise a driver's awareness of the limitations that hold him back, helping his perceptions.**

Nowadays it's easier to know a great deal about the car's potential, because we can use simulation tools and a driving simulator to predict lap time in many different conditions. This is an incredible step forward, compared to when lap times were unknown until the tires hit the asphalt. These days a driver can test the gears in every corner, refresh his marks and do setup work in advance – all of this with a high degree of accuracy.

When using simulation tools, we need to rely on the accuracy of vehicle and track models. In this respect the standard is quite high in all the top series, but this is something we'll discuss in greater detail in the last chapter.

My experience in vehicle modeling and simulation has taught me that a model, no matter how good it is, will always be different from the real car – and the best thing a driver can do is understand and accept this.

I am always taken aback when I hear some drivers telling the engineers after a simulator run: "This is different from the real car, I can't drive it". It shouldn't come as a surprise, since by definition a simulation model is different from the real car: it's a mathematical set of equations that try to represent the behavior of a very complex system. Unfortunately, regardless of the accuracy of the models, a driver will never drive the simulator exactly as he would drive the real car – the emotional part of the experience will always be missing.

Imagine having the perfect vehicle model and the perfect motion platform, able to provide the driver with the same cues as a real car. Even in such an ideal situation there would still be an element missing from the simulation: the risk associated with a real race. How can you possibly simulate that?

Once, when I was working on a simulator project, I was asked to model the vehicle's contact with a wall, so the platform would shake if the driver went beyond the track limits. In American racing series, walls are a big challenge for the drivers, in both street circuits and ovals. We spent a good deal of time implementing the right logic into the software, testing the feedback level from the platform and enhancing the experience with this additional cue. We soon realized that it was a useful addition to street circuits, because it helped the driver respect the limits and take a more realistic approach with the simulator. For ovals, on the other hand, it was useless, simply because if you hit the wall in an oval, the consequences are much more serious than a little bump and shake from a simulator platform. No matter what solutions we apply in this case, you will always get closer to the wall in a simulator than on the real track, since the risk of getting hurt is not there.

We shouldn't forget that simulators offer an experience that is a representation of reality. This experience can be useful only if the driver accepts the fact that he's driving a vehicle model on a track model and is feeling artificial cues. The right mindset is to consider it as a tool for the team to collect information that can be useful in preparing for an event or for car development. Later in the book we'll see that it can also help drivers practice and train their skills.

Every track presents a special challenge, and even if you go back to it year after year, it will always be different from the last time you were there. Back in the days when these tools were not available, it was a different story – the driver just jumped in the car and worked his way through the weekend. Today's technology has changed everything: now preparation for the weekend starts at the factory, where the driver (or a dedicated simulator driver) can try the car and do setup work in a virtual environment in the days leading up to the weekend.

I have had experience of this kind of preparation sessions with many drivers in different categories, from NASCAR to IndyCar, Formula 1, LMP1, the series that are currently named F2 and F3, the old European F3, Indy Lights and Super Formula. While attending these sessions I've had the privilege of observing different approaches to the use of the simulator.

Some sessions went well, but others were fraught with problems and became messier than a test day at the track. Still, no matter how straightforward or complex a session was, I have always seen drivers walking out with more information than they came in with in the morning.

The simulator can be a good tool to improve a driver's awareness of the car's potential. It can provide some important information about a specific circuit, such as:

- Predominant understeer or oversteer behavior
- The level of bumpiness of the circuit

- Bottoming limits

- Downforce level

- Fuel management and tire management with different downforce levels

- Balance shift prediction (active tire thermal and wear models)

- Tire degradation limiting corners (front left, front right, rear left or rear right)

- Tire temperature management strategies

- The wind effect from different directions

- Brake management consequences

- Overtake possibilities

The list could get longer and will vary depending on the event and the car we're preparing. In general, with the help of simulations and data from the previous year we can find answers to all these key points, allowing the driver to have a clearer idea of the car's potential and a better reading once he is inside the car.

Let's look at an example. If you were preparing for a World Endurance Championship event with an LMP1, LMP2 or GT car, you would focus on the following points:

- Traffic management strategies

- Optimizing energy per lap when encountering traffic (in the case of LMP1-H, for instance)

- Finding the best setup for the three drivers

- Target lap time for the night stints

- Practicing night scenarios

- Tire management for triple or quadruple stints.

On the other hand, if we were preparing for an oval race with an Indy car or a NASCAR car, there might be different points to consider, such as:

- Weight jacker sensitivity for cross weight tuning

- Anti-roll bars adjustment sensitivity on car balance

- Aero balance sensitivity on tire wear

- Fuel saving strategies

- Lift & coast to cover for possible cautions

- Engine boost deployment strategies and scenarios

- Changing only the left-hand tires rather than all four tires.

In addition to this, for example, when driving a Formula E car, we also need to consider the issue of energy management.

Clearly, **each type of racing has different requirements, which is something that many people frequently underestimate. Even an experienced driver will need to go back and look at the whole picture from a completely different point of view if he decides to switch from a racing series to another.**

Fernando Alonso's recent experience with Toyota in LMP1 is quite a good example. I had the pleasure of working with him in his first track test in Bahrain back in 2017. His approach was exemplary in many ways. When we had some preparation sessions with the simulator at the factory, it was inspiring to see his openness to absorb information and suggestions, his natural interest in learning from us how to tame the new beast he was driving. We were working on one specific corner which required a very different approach compared to what he was used to with a Formula 1 car. I felt a bit awkward giving a two-time World Champion of his caliber advice on how to correct his driving, and yet I felt I had all his attention – he was totally focused on what I was telling him. Once it was clear to him that Michelin tires had a different response to combined grip compared to Formula 1 Pirelli tires, he understood that he had to adapt. It took him just two laps to be on top of it, and two more to be faster than his reference. He was really impressive!

If a driver is aware of the car performance envelope, he can frame any possible limitations and scenarios he might encounter. This enables him to prepare for them and start thinking about possible countermeasures.

Being a performance engineer in a fast-paced environment like Formula 1 has taught me the importance of preparing before the weekend. Similarly to drivers, engineers also need to be ready to react to different challenges, which requires a massive amount of work before the race weekend. Most of it is dedicated to collecting all the information that can be useful, which is then shared with the driver and the rest of the team. On the basis of this information, we discuss actions in response to certain limitations and decide what needs to be tested. **All the people working on a car need to have the plan clear in their mind before the race weekend, because when the practice session starts there is no time to spare.**

It's essential for an engineer to be on top of this: before the start of the first free practice, any possible balance issues need to be addressed and any setup changes planned in advance, so as to be ready for every foreseeable scenario. We all know that a surprise is always around the corner, so we'd better be prepared.

It's fundamental for a driver handling cutting-edge-technology race cars to have a clear idea of all the options he has when it comes to setup and controls. I am now deliberately steering toward those series where controls have a greater impact, such as Formula 1, LMP1 and Formula E.

When I talk about controls, I mean all those options that can be tuned by onboard switch changes and can be remapped via cable when the car is in the garage. In hybrid or electric race cars we have brake-by-wire systems that allow us to shape the brake balance with the driver's input – and these maps can be tuned live. The active differential lets us play with the rate of opening and locking to fine-tune the wheel speed separation around the track – not to mention engine braking or front-to-rear motor priority to adjust balance settings or affect tire wear. These are just a few examples of onboard controls that the driver can actively influence.

The behavior of Formula 1, LMP1 or Formula E cars is highly dependent on their control system settings. For a driver it can be a great advantage to be fully aware of what is available to him in terms of controls: this will help him to manage a trend in the car balance over the distance of a race, or to solve a balance limitation with a few clicks on his steering wheel, rather than waiting for a mechanical or aero setup change.

Ultimately, a driver who is able to master all the controls that are available to him will end up being faster than another driver who drives the same car without these specific skills.

Endurance racing provides the best example of this, because it requires the driver to share his car with two other drivers. There are not many excuses when you compare your performance with that of your team mates. Given that the car is the same, you put new tires on for each driver and the track conditions are similar, the delta lap time will tell you all you need to know. You can rest assured that not being on top of those control options will definitely make one driver slower than his team mates – and we are not talking about hundredths of a second.

In other series – like Formula 1, IndyCar, NASCAR or Formula E – the cars driven by two team mates will always be different, even if they're meant to start with very similar cars. However, it's impossible for two cars to be exactly the same. In this kind of comparison, you can come up with so many caveats that in the end you never get a conclusive result – one car will always be faster than the other.

From personal experience, I can tell you that no driver takes it well when he realizes that he is slower than his team mate, especially if there is a big gap between them!

Drivers who aspire to approach the pinnacle of motorsport may be interested to know some of the most common control settings that can be found on the steering wheel:

- Brake shape maps

- Engine braking / Pedal maps

- Differential maps

- Traction controls

- Understeer modifiers

- Fuel strategy maps

- Energy boost maps

Traction control – which is prohibited in Formula 1, but allowed in other series – requires a different driving style and a different approach to the management of tire degradation. It is generally regulated with a switch change.

The possibilities are so many that a whole book could be written just on this topic. In this context I just want to highlight that it's best practice for a driver to understand what tools are available to him and to know the pros and cons of each one of them in different scenarios.

Some tools have a similar balance effect, but they will hurt one thing or another. A good driver will want to have this clear in his mind in order to be able to master the whole situation.

Clearly this is not an easy task – experience teaches us that it requires time and practice to get on top of it. Even an experienced driver needs to discuss the key controls with the performance engineer and the control engineer, so as to prepare for the main scenarios and the possible changes to be made to correct the balance.

On this note, I'd like to quote a very good statement I heard Kevin Magnussen make in a driver's debrief: "These tools are so powerful that you can make a bad car perform well, if you know what you're doing with them".

## The Evaluation of External Factors

Changes in the weather and the wind, track evolution, tire degradation, a safety car and a Full Course Yellow are some of the most likely challenges that a driver could face. Like every challenge, they also represent a potential opportunity that we can use to our advantage, for the purpose of gaining time.

Being prepared for these situations is of crucial importance, because even the remotest possibility could become real. Although it is certainly not feasible to forecast all the possible scenarios, it's good practice for a driver to analyze as many of them as possible with his team.

If he had to manage one of the situations envisioned in advance, he would be sharper in recognizing them, because he would have already thought about them. This would help him manage his emotions and ultimately lead him to a better decision and a faster reaction.

Some of the main possibilities that a driver should evaluate beforehand – as well as review once they have happened – are:

- Changes in environmental conditions, rain or wind
- Track evolution: dry to wet or wet to dry
- Changes in the temperature of the track
- Track evolution due to rubber on the asphalt
- The transition from day to night conditions and vice versa
- Flags
- Safety cars
- Punctures.

A change in boundaries is hard to deal with in every business, because it brings us out of our comfort zone, tests our mental toughness and challenges our ability to react and adapt to change.

Let me give you an example from an LMP1 Endurance race. In that series you may encounter a Full Course Yellow (FCY) situation, in which safety reasons dictate that all cars have to adhere to specific limitations. If you're driving an LMP1-H car, you have a maximum amount of energy you can discharge per lap – energy that activates the electric motors and increases the power by about 300 kW (~ 408 cv). If the FCY comes up when you're halfway through the lap, you will lose the possibility of deploying the amount of energy you would have deployed in the last part of the lap, thus wasting potential lap time.

What is peculiar to the Endurance Championship is that when the race director decides for a Full Course Yellow, every team gets a heads-up and a 10-second countdown from Race Control before it becomes effective. In this type of situation, the smart thing to do is to manually boost all your battery energy up to the maximum limit per lap as soon as possible. Even if you don't use it in the most sensitive part of the track, this still brings you a gain on anyone who doesn't do the same.

If there are two drivers racing similar cars, the one who is better prepared and aware of this possibility will inevitably do better. He will promptly deploy the energy, boosting and emptying the battery as soon as he gets the message of an FCY coming in 10 seconds. I have seen this happening more than once during my experience with the LMP1-H Toyota TS050: the lap time gains can be counted in seconds thanks to a simple action like this.

In a situation like this, the driver's awareness makes all the difference. His level of attention will rise instantly because he recognizes a pattern in the succession of events, a scenario he has already seen and discussed while preparing for the weekend with the engineers. **In a challenging scenario, in which a driver is under all the pressure that a race involves, it isn't easy to be clear-headed about what** is happening. **Each individual will have different emotions and reactions, but preparation is of paramount importance.**

A sudden change – such as a safety car or a puncture, for example – will invalidate everything he has done up to that point and force him out of his comfort zone. **A driver needs to learn how to be comfortably uncomfortable to survive and succeed.**

## The Athlete's Psychological Preparation

Over the years I have noticed common behavioral patterns in the way professional drivers deal with emotions, mistakes and achievements – their response to stressful events is an intriguing part of their characters. **Once a driver finds the key to the mental zone that allows him to master the unexpected, he can unlock and exploit his potential to the full.**

The main obstacle professional athletes, and race drivers in particular, have to overcome is an instinctive reluctance to accept that there is nothing wrong with seeking external help to improve the way they approach their tasks. Racing is considered a "macho" sport and it's not a secret that drivers are generally afraid of showing weakness when they accept to work on their mental performance. This was certainly true in the past (and not only in motor racing), but luckily social attitudes are changing in this respect and drivers are now more willing to train their mental as well as their physical abilities.

Nowadays it's not uncommon for a driver to be supported by a performance coach, or by one of the engineers who, among other duties, can also help him from a psychological point of view. Each driver is different from the others and has his own doubts and fears, so there isn't a common recipe for their psychological well-being. As we said before, **all three phases of the P-D-R® process strongly depend on a solid and healthy cognitive and emotional background. This aspect is of paramount importance for unlocking a driver's full potential.**

Psychological performance and mental toughness can be taught and trained. There are highly specialized personal and mental coaches who work with lots of professional athletes, achieving great results. I will refrain from attempting to provide an in-depth analysis of psychological training in this text – I'll leave this to the experts and to the existing literature. However, I would like to elaborate on a few key points that influence a driver's psychological condition.

One of the most recent and broadly used methods to represent an athlete's mental condition is the Performance Pyramid. This is a bottom-to-top representation of the most influential mental abilities that a professional athlete needs to master. The concept of the pyramid is effective because, as we all know by now, the human mind works better when it can subdivide its big challenges into smaller tasks. In our case, of course, we are going to focus on race drivers and adapt the pyramid to their specific requirements.

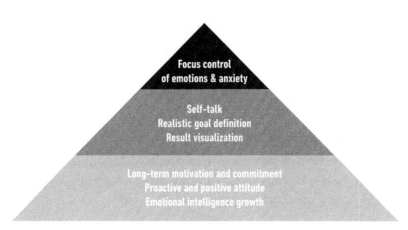

*Figure 2.1: The Performance Pyramid*

The three levels of the pyramid don't just contain different skills, but also represent three different moments in the driver's life and the different levels of pressure associated with them.

1. The Green **(or lower) Level** represents the basic skill set that an athlete will need to apply in his daily routine. These characteristics become part of a driver's lifestyle and are commonly useful in low-pressure and low-anxiety situations.

2. The Orange **(or intermediate) Level** skills are required before a performance, which includes not only competition races, but every single event where the driver needs to perform – a free practice, a qualifying session, a meeting or some media duties. The level of pressure and anxiety associated with this phase is higher than at the green level.

3. The **Red (or top) Level** skills are the ones a driver needs to apply during a performance – a free practice, a qualifying ses-

sion or a race. Of course, the highest level of pressure and anxiety is experienced during this phase.

**A driver's psychological condition will affect the way he manages stress and anxiety and will define his main interactions with the people around him. The target is to master those feelings and achieve control over all the positive and negative thoughts that might compromise the key moments in his professional life.**

If you're a sportsperson and have had the opportunity of taking part in a competition, you know how important it is to be in control of the emotions and anxieties involved in competitions. Before a performance, your nerves are tense and adrenaline pumps into your body. You try to keep your tension under control and to hide it from other people, but the pressure is there – you know that it's time to deliver what you and your team have been working so hard for.

Anybody who thinks that a driver won't be affected by this does not really know human nature. Even if he has been through this many times, it's not possible for a driver to get used to it and consider it business as usual.

When I walk around the Formula 1 paddock on Sunday mornings, before a race, I can perceive that something is different from free practice days. Those carefree smiles the drivers had on the previous days are gone and the tension clearly shows on their faces. Whenever they have a free moment in their busy schedule, they try to clear their minds and concentrate.

In Indianapolis, during the crucial month of May, you see people walking up and down Gasoline Alley for the Indy Grand Prix first and later for the Indy 500 free practice days, qualifying sessions, Carb Day, until the day of the race arrives. That's when it all moves up to a different level: it's not playtime anymore, it's time to get in the zone, because the most important race of the year is about to start. This race is worth a whole year for the driver who gets the checkered flag first.

I have often noticed this change in the drivers' behavior and I can still see it today on race days. They are there with you, they listen to the briefing, they answer and they are active parts of their team – yet their attitude is slightly different from the days before. The pressure increases minute after minute, and they start thinking of all the possible scenarios, wondering if they are going to be fast enough, good enough, skillful enough to manage what is about to happen. It is the same with me and the other engineers and mechanics, in every motorsport environment. The level of anxiety spreads out to all the people involved, in proportion to the amount of responsibility each of us has. When it comes to those events that are worth a whole season, like the Indy 500 or Le Mans, it is even harder.

Some drivers let their thoughts go to a place where they can find calm and peace, because they know that the storm is about to start. It's a storm of feelings, emotions, adrenaline and thoughts flashing in their brains faster than the speed of light. Yet they need to keep everything under control – their rational part and their subconscious have to work together. They perceive everything that is happening around them, make decisions and react, both consciously and instinctively, as described in the Perception-Decision-Reaction® process.

**We will consider the Performance Pyramid as the sum of the skills that need to be trained to develop the mental toughness required to be a successful professional driver.**

**The Performance Pyramid skills can be seen as the foundation to the P-D-R® process. Since every single skill in the pyramid is a key development point for the driver's growth, his training needs to focus on each different level and associate it with the appropriate amount of pressure.** This way, the driver can gradually get used to it.

A driver's mental preparation is as important as his physical condition. As we all know, in every athlete's career there are bound to be highs and lows. Athletes who manage to achieve a certain level of mental toughness are able to thrive through difficult moments – and this is a key skill that can be trained and improved.

# KEY POINTS

- The first phase of the P-D-R® process relates to Perception, which represents much more than just feeling the movement of the car: it is a wider concept of perception, which hinges on the overall preparation of the driver, so he can be ready to face different scenarios.

- There are four key points to work on in order to improve a driver's perception: balance evaluation, awareness of the car's performance and controls, the evaluation of external factors and the athlete's psychological condition.

- The importance of a driver's preparation for his perception ability has been analyzed to identify the key points to develop for the purpose of improving his overall performance.

- There is a close connection between a driver's mental performance and the P-D-R® process. The Performance Pyramid shows the key skill set required to achieve the mental toughness a driver needs to succeed. A strong and healthy mental condition will have a positive impact on all three phases of the driving process.

# 3 THE DECISION PHASE

Zandvoort 2021.
Courtesy of F1-Fansite.com

DURING A RACE, IT'S ESSENTIAL FOR DRIVERS TO AVOID ANY UNCERTAINTY AND INDECISION, OTHERWISE THEY'LL FREEZE AND WON'T BE ABLE TO SEE ANY OF THE SOLUTIONS AVAILABLE – WHICH IS SOMETHING THEY SIMPLY CANNOT AFFORD.

The second phase of the P-D-R® process concerns the ability to make a decision. Whichever sport they practice, professional athletes share one important skill: they are excellent decision makers, who are able to control what happens rather than letting things happen to them.

In motor racing, we can identify two main types of decision:

- static decisions
- dynamic decisions

Static decisions are focused on the car and are not strictly related to driving. They can concern racing issues – like setup directions, run plan preferences and race strategies – or business issues – like media appearances, answers given to interviewers, contract discussions, and so on. In these circumstances the driver can control his emotions and has plenty of time to calmly evaluate all his options.

Dynamic decisions, on the other hand, are much harder, because a driver needs to make them while driving. The fundamental difference between the two types of decision is that a dynamic decision needs to be made in a matter of seconds and there are no second chances. These decisions are going to be the main focus of our analysis.

However, **every single decision, regardless of the category it falls into, has an impact on a driver's performance: a badly-chosen answer in an interview, a wrong decision on setup direction or an argument over a contract can easily compromise a racing weekend.** That's why it's essential for a driver to be well prepared to avoid making wrong choices, as well as ready to change direction in case he realizes he has made a mistake. This will give him a clear advantage over his competitors.

First of all, I'd like to clarify that when I talk about dynamic decisions, I am not referring to a driver's instinctive reaction to keep control of the car when oversteering over a curb. This is a type of situation in which you don't have any time to think, so it falls into the category of instinctive reactions. In this case, the driver receives all the information he needs directly in the perception phase. We are going to look at this later in the book, when we examine instinctive reactions in greater detail.

Decision making is an essential skill for an athlete, so it should be trained and improved over time. Taking an engineering approach, we are going to break down the decision phase into key areas to improve our understanding and training tactics related to each one of them.

Every decision process can be divided into two separate parts, which are based on the succession of events: real time and post-performance. The first part concerns all those aspects that influence us and help us understand what to do in the moments when we are making our decisions. The post-performance phase comes after the decision, once we are in a different state of mind and not under so much stress. Although this part of the process is fundamental, its importance is sometimes underestimated.

Within each part we can discern the following key areas:

- Real time
  - Problem analysis
  - Exploring the options available
  - Choosing the best option
- Post-performance
  - Decision review and accountability.

Post-performance analysis is a necessary part of the decision process. We have often seen athletes making choices that didn't help them in any way or even caused them additional problems, only to see them make the same decisions again at a later stage. This means that they didn't take the time to review the process that had led them to make that choice and therefore didn't realize that it was the wrong decision. Alternatively, they may have realized that it was a bad decision, but didn't understand the root cause of their behavior. As a consequence, they didn't learn from their mistake and were likely to repeat it.

## Problem Analysis

We have already seen that the P-D-R® model can follow two different paths – standard or instinctive. The standard path can be considered a low-frequency process, while the instinctive path is faster because it short-cuts from perception to reaction. The decision phase takes place only in the standard process, so our remarks in this chapter apply to this type of process. Later in the book we'll see how the instinctive dynamic works and when it applies.

It's important to remember, though, that in the continuous action of driving, these two processes happen simultaneously.

The output of the perception phase is the combined result of a driver's preparation, experience and psychological condition. In the standard process, the perception output will contain all the information he needs in order to analyze a problem.

Detail-oriented preparation work teaches a driver to understand if the data that reach the decisional area contain all that is necessary to make a decision. It's easy to appreciate how important a driver's preparation is. If it's superficial, he will base his decision on missing or incorrect data, which is bound to lead to a suboptimal choice.

**We shouldn't forget that every single action counts: racing is a highly competitive sport, in which every wrong choice slows down the driver and makes him less effective than those who instead made the right one.**

Problem analysis consists in cross-checking all the information available with the context we are dealing with and the outcome we want to achieve. The final goal is to raise the driver's awareness in a specific situation and construct a series of connections between a problem and all the actions that can be taken to deal with it.

Preparation is not always enough to solve a problem – no matter how well we prepare, we may not have all the information required to solve a specific issue. Moreover, emotions and stress can have a strong impact on this phase, so a driver needs to be able to manage his emotions to get a clear, objective view of what is going on.

However, there is room for success even when there isn't a proper match between the problem and the network of information available. In this case, the driver and his team need to use their judgment. The element of trust is essential: when it's necessary to make an assessment with limited resources available, a driver has to trust both this own judgment and his team's.

In this type of scenario, the engineers will issue some clear instructions, or alternatively the driver will make a sound independent decision. This is when the kind of preparation the team has gone through when planning the weekend really make a difference: if the general attitude has been oriented toward taking risks, there is room for dangerous options, while if the approach has been more conservative, the team will tend to go for a safer option.

Whatever decision is taken, it may turn out to be wrong. It happens. However, before making any choice, it's always important to assess the situation to the best of your ability.

Let me give you an example from my own experience. Imagine you are one of the drivers taking part in the 24h of Le Mans. You're easily in the lead when going for the last lap, but suddenly you perceive an engine problem – you are losing power. Do you remember what happened to the Toyota team at the 2016 edition of the infamous French endurance race? It would be an understatement to say that the driver experienced a stressful, heart-breaking situation. Kazuki Nakajima was behind the wheel for the last stint – concentrated on trying to bring it home, staying clear from the curbs, calculating the risk at each corner and listening to every little noise the car made. He was fully in the zone.

When the seemingly impossible happened, Kazuki's reaction was remarkable. As soon as he felt there was a problem, he reported it back. Then he displayed nerves of steel by managing to keep it together and doing step by step what the team asked him to do. It was a desperate attempt to power cycle the car, in the hope that the problem could be fixed this way.

That was a very brave decision. The car was still running – though at reduced speed – and he was just one lap away from making history, but he knew that it probably wouldn't be enough to beat the Porsche LMP1-H. So he decided to follow to the letter the instructions he was given.

We were able to attempt a power cycle only thanks to Kazuki's ability to control his emotions, which must have been utterly overwhelming. Although he could feel that a historical win was slipping through his hands, he analyzed the situation in his mind and understood that he had more chances of finishing the race by following the team's instructions – and so he did. The ultimate goal of finishing the race was clear in his mind and he simply focused on it, displaying an incredible awareness of the situation he was in.

Unfortunately, there was no happy ending that time. After the power cycle, once the engine was shut off, the car didn't restart and ended up stuck in front of the pit wall. We had to witness Porsche taking away the victory from us.

We tried to complete the last lap in full electric mode, in order to finish the race at least. Imagine how distressing the situation was: although the race was already lost, Kazuki was still doing all he could to get the car to the finishing line. Since it took him more than the maximum time allowed after the checkered flag, we were disqualified. Le Mans is a tough, ruthless race.

I'm sure that later on Kazuki asked himself if he had made the wrong choice. There is only one answer to this question: it was the choice that made the most sense to him and the team at the time, which is why that decision was made.

Summing up, **when you have a clear perception of the situation, a good analysis of the problem – considering both the context you're dealing with and the goal you're aiming for – will increase your awareness and open the way to the exploration of all available options.**

A driver needs to focus on his ultimate goal, otherwise he risks being overwhelmed by his emotions. It is crucial for him to be able to control his emotions and any possible anxiety – a decision is necessarily linked to uncertainty, which always creates discomfort, so a good psychological condition is a prerequisite for a successful performance.

## Exploring All Available Options

When it's time to explore the options available, a driver already has a clear idea of what is happening around him, thanks to the perception phase and his analysis of the problem. At this point, he needs to keep his emotions under control and look at all the alternatives that are available to him.

Making a decision doesn't necessarily mean changing anything: there is just as much decisional power in keeping things as they are. The first option to consider is that of maintaining the status quo, holding steady and letting events run their course. This is a possibility that we should always consider proactively rather than letting events take control of our emotions and force us to change course without any real reason.

In these circumstances, **our most valuable resources are experience, preparation and mental toughness. They will help us evaluate the options to choose from and lower our level of anxiety, so that we are able to think properly.** Having too many alternatives is a real possibility, but this is a risk that a driver can't afford to run – he can make sense of the situation in a very short time only if he has a limited number of options.

To make sure we are well prepared when it's time to explore our options, we should consider the following focus points:

- Pre-event preparation for the most likely scenarios. This will allow the driver to become familiar with the different options available to him in case a problem arises. This means that when one of these scenarios becomes a reality, he will already know what his options are. Here are some examples of race scenarios that it's worth considering beforehand:

- Choice of tires during the race
- Car balance adjustments during the race (chassis and controls)
- Pit stop lap considerations over track position
- Car damage at some point in the race
- Yellow Flags / cautions at some point in the race
- Puncture
- First lap car damage.

- Maintaining an open conversation with the engineers in case of unexpected scenarios. This will help us to cover those situations that occur unexpectedly and could easily catch us unprepared. It doesn't have to be a conclusive elaboration of all possible options – it's just a matter of developing a sense of the alternatives available, so as to prioritize accordingly.

  - Some issues to consider are:
  - Engagement rules with other cars or with your team mate
  - Defending a certain position, risk assessment over track position
  - Brake management over track position

· Fuel management over track position

· Dry to wet transition or vice versa.

In my opinion, unknown problems are the most delicate ones, because there is a high chance of being caught off guard and seeing yourself out of the race. This is the reason why we try to consider as many possible scenarios as we can – **envisaging unlikely events is an effective way of improving the team's reliability.**

A good example of this is an episode from my endurance racing experience: during the 2017 edition of the 24 Hours of Le Mans I learned that there is no such thing as an impossible scenario.

Kamui Kobayashi was driving the number #7 LMP1-H Toyota and we were entering the night around the 10th hour. We were easily in the lead: the car was a rocket and the three drivers – Kamui, Mike Conway and Jose M. Lopez – had been extremely fast during the build-up to the race. A safety car was deployed for an accident, and since it was a good moment for us, we pitted for a full service, fuel and tires. Kamui was waiting at the pit exit for a green light to follow the safety car, when a driver from an LMP2 team suddenly walked out in front of Kamui and gave him a thumbs-up to congratulate him on the great job he was doing. Given that he was wearing an orange, marshal-style race suit and a helmet, Kamui – who was waiting for the green light in the darkness of the night – mistook him for a marshal giving him the okay to clear the pit lane. Thinking that the pit exit light was malfunctioning, he started the car. Of course, when we realized that he was about to leave the pit lane with a red light, we stopped him immediately.

To understand what happened next, you should know that LMP1-H cars start with an electric motor pull-away; then the driver turns on the internal combustion engine by releasing the clutch and spinning the engine, exactly as Kamui did. When we stopped him, he braked and pressed the clutch, with the internal combustion engine running, waiting for our okay to go. Seconds later we cleared him to leave the pit exit and he performed a conventional start – the same type of start that people like us perform when the traffic light goes green. Unfortunately, the clutch got damaged because the operating conditions were more stressful than expected: it was almost completely burned – and our chances of winning that infamous race went up in smoke once again.

The unpredictability of this event forced the team to review the way we prepare. It became clear that we had to envisage all possible scenarios, including the most unlikely ones we could imagine. We started focusing on preparing the drivers and the team for a number of unpredictable events. Clearly, it's very difficult to foresee and train for something if you are not even aware that it could happen, but there is much that can be done. You can prepare on multiple levels, with accurate fault tree analysis processes, during endurance testing and simulator tests. That year we worked very hard on this – and as a result, the following year the team finally managed to grab the long-dreamed-of trophy!

Different categories may present different challenges, but **the goal is the same: simulating pressure-packed scenarios to force the team to understand the issues and evaluate the options available in the shortest time possible. This means learning well all the procedures we can anticipate, preparing for any imaginable situation, and at the same time gaining confidence in our ability to read a situation, control our emotions and thrive when an unexpected challenge arrives.**

Once again, training is the answer.

## Choosing the Best Option

When it's time to make a decision, a driver has to select the most effective option among all the ones that are available to him. This may sound like the most difficult step in the decision-making process, but we shouldn't forget that by the time he gets to this point, he has already analyzed the problem and explored all his options. Therefore, all he has to do now is put together all the pieces of the puzzle.

Any choice involves a compromise: even the simplest decision we make in our everyday lives is the result of a more or less conscious analysis of its pros and cons. We often spend more time than we should thinking of reasons to do or not to do something.

**During a race, it's essential for drivers to avoid any uncertainty and indecision, otherwise they'll freeze and won't be able to**

see any of the solutions available – which is something they simply cannot afford.

To avoid a deadlock and start considering all his options, a driver needs to turn to his inner resources:

- focusing on the final goal

- team vision

- previous experiences

- effective practice sessions.

His decisions will be based on his inner resources and the information he has at the time of deciding.

**Making a choice is essentially a process that helps us eliminate the worst options. It's a process that requires sangfroid, a solid psychological condition, focus and control of our emotions. All these mental skills are needed to isolate the problem from everything that is not relevant, process it and make the best possible choice.**

Nowadays we have access to the radio exchanges between Formula 1 engineers and drivers. While the general public can only access some of them, people who work in the business can hear all of them, if they want. The way drivers and engineers communicate with this tool clearly needs to be different from a normal conversation – engineers have to send messages that are short, clear and definitive, because the person they are talking to is coping with a lot of pressure while driving at dangerously high speed. It's important to avoid giving irrelevant or confusing information, which would make the situation even harder for the driver.

I won't talk about the bad examples of radio exchanges that you can easily find online, because we need to know their full context to understand why there was such tension. I would rather focus my attention on those rare exchanges in which you can barely perceive any tension between the speakers. These are rare but precious examples of drivers and engineers discussing which decision to make with surprising calm.

Having heard radio messages from lots of different drivers in disparate categories, I can assure you that it's really amazing to hear a driver who is so calm that you almost can't believe he's actually driving at 200 mph.

Lewis Hamilton's team radio provides many good examples of this, which can easily be found online. When you listen to them it's difficult to perceive any tension in his voice – he never loses his cool when talking to his engineer, who is just as calm as him. We shouldn't forget that their exchanges are usually about major decisions, which can have a decisive impact on winning a Formula 1 race or even a championship.

Let's look at the Mercedes team radio from the 2016 Abu Dhabi race, in which Lewis and Nico Rosberg were competing for the championship. Lewis was winning the race, but he could win the

World Championship only if his team mate, Nico, finished in third place. Nico was second, trying to stop Sebastian Vettel's Ferrari from passing him for second place. Suddenly it became clear that Lewis was intentionally slowing down to help Vettel pass Nico.

The team's technical director was very clear when he spoke to Lewis on the radio: "Lewis, this is Paddy. We need you to pick up the pace to win this race. That's an instruction".

Lewis's answer was: "Paddy, I am actually in the lead right now and I am quite comfortable where I am. I am losing the World Championship, so I am not really bothered if I win or lose this race".

These words were pronounced with the sort of detachment that we certainly wouldn't expect from someone that, at the end of a very demanding season, was losing the championship to his team mate. Yet he was calm and lucid enough to understand that it was his last chance to get the title.

Lewis was focused on his goal, understood the situation very well and was fully aware of the consequences that his decision would have at the end of the race. He deliberately tried to compromise his team and his team mate's result to win the title. Was it an unpopular move? Maybe, but it took a lot of guts to make this kind of choice, given the possible outcomes. As Ayrton Senna once said, "if you no longer go for a gap that exists, you are no longer a racing driver".

Lewis Hamilton did everything he could to win, but he still lost the championship to Nico Rosberg. He had no regrets, though, because he knew that he had left no stone unturned to achieve his goal.

**Choosing what we believe to be the best option will always involve a risk. We need to be fully aware of this before making any decisions, because we'll be held accountable for their outcome. There is always a fine balance between risks and rewards, and it's up to us to weigh them up and decide how to proceed. Clearly this is not something that a driver can learn overnight. It requires a lot of experience, including errors of judgment and wrong choices that will gradually help him improve his decision-making skills.**

A race driver must calculate risk according to what is at stake. This will shape the decision process and lead him toward the best option he has to achieve the advantage he is looking for.

## Decision Review and Accountability

The last key point in the driver's decision-making process is review and accountability. This step involves looking back at his choices with a critical eye, proactively looking for a lesson to learn from them. It's essential for a driver to go through this last part in order to close the loop of his decision process. **Making a choice should never the final step: if we want to learn something new that we can use in the future, we also need to review our decision.**

During the review and accountability phase drivers need to be aware of the following points:

**Mistakes happen, and they should be seen as opportunities for growth.** Of course, it's always upsetting to realize that we have made a mistake, but once we get over the disappointment and the anger, we need to use them as learning opportunities.

- **Mistakes are not a necessary condition for learning – achievements are just as important.** Once the happiness and satisfaction for the good result have faded, it's time to reconsider all the factors that have contributed to our success, so as to see what we could have done even better.

- **A good review process needs to use the emotional variable in a constructive way.** Feeling disappointed, angry, happy, or satisfied is a natural part of being a professional athlete (and a human being). We will always be exposed to these emotional states, so it's important to be able to control them and take advantage of them.

Associating an emotion to something we have learned in our review will make the lesson more useful and easier to remember. As an example, if poor judgment has led us to make a mistake, the feeling of disappointment we associate to the lesson we have learned will contribute to preventing us from repeating the same mistake. **It's crucial to be proactive and use our emotions to achieve our goals instead of being passively overwhelmed by them. Otherwise, emotions will cloud our judgment and limit our choices and those of the people around us.**

A driver who is not afraid to show his emotions and is honest with himself and other people will enhance the team's performance, because the other members will be more inclined to do the same.

It's worth devoting a few lines to the positive moments that follow a success or a special accomplishment. When a driver is happy with his performance and his choices, he needs to share that positive energy with all members of his team and anybody who has helped him succeed. If he keeps it for himself and takes all the credit, he is bound to waste these wonderful emotions – which, if channeled properly, would push the people around him to do even better, giving him a great advantage.

Another essential part of a performance review is accountability, i.e. taking responsibility for your actions. A driver needs to remember that he is the person that everyone looks up to. Acknowledging his own responsibilities when something goes wrong will drive his team to do the same when they happen to be at fault.

There are plenty of examples of a driver's actions hurting his team, as well as situations in which a driver was hurt by his team's misjudgments or mistakes. It's part of the game. **In a winning team there is no room for finger pointing: when something goes wrong, it needs to be properly understood so we can prevent it from happening again.** When you have a successful mindset, there is never any need to blame other people – whoever has made a mistake will apologize and learn from it.

In my career I have made a few mistakes. It's only natural, and I have always admitted to them in front of my bosses and my drivers. It helps to find closure and get over the distress and discomfort you feel when you realize you've made the wrong decision. This is very important, because we need to regain our clarity of thought as soon as possible in order to analyze what has happened and learn from it.

In most racing categories a first review is typically done right after the event, in the driver's debrief meeting. This is the best time for a review, as long as there are no emotions clouding our judgment. Otherwise we need to wait to cool off our temper and maybe review only the points we know won't be affected by our emotions. This way we can avoid saying things that we don't really mean just because of the heat of the moment, which would make the review counterproductive. After all, we can always go over the other points in a second moment.

Sometimes there is nothing useful a driver can add about a topic, which is not a problem – he can mention any issues later on, if he feels there is something worth saying.

**Training sessions are essential for boosting a driver's decision-making skills, because they provide a safe environment in which he can become aware of the consequences of a choice over another. This is when he has the opportunity to make mistakes and correct them without any consequences.**

In motorsport there are fewer and fewer tests during training days, so drivers mostly train with simulators and personal trainers. The good news is that these sessions offer them the opportunity to make plenty of decisions involving achievement and failure, which can be useful for developing their grasp of the decision-making process.

Practicing additional, unrelated sports is also useful, but it's still important to take time for a general review at the end of any performance, including the following key points:

- Considering which actions have given the biggest gain or loss

- Focusing on specific decisions

- Discussing the performance, asking for other people's opinions

- Acknowledging and sharing what could have been done better.

These general points apply not only to the athletes, but also to the people around them. After a training session or a race, it's useful for an engineer or a mechanic to re-examine what happened and if there is any margin for improvement. One of the first things I learned when I started working in this industry is that there is always something new to learn down the road.

**The review process will improve a driver's self-awareness and enhance his ability to read a situation, making it easier for him to handle it the next time. It will help him identify his strengths, limitations, motivations and goals.**

It's worth mentioning that the engineers, the personal trainer and the general environment around a driver will affect his attitude toward taking responsibilities. The best results can be achieved if the driver is able to create a sort of safe area around him – a place where he feels comfortable enough to share and discuss his ideas, feelings and actions with others in a constructive way. This is generally known as Steady Sport Coaching Style, a coaching style that involves more than two-way communication. It's an approach that pushes athletes to evaluate their own performance and accept the advice and constructive feedback provided by their team as part of their own development.

The protection guaranteed by this safe area will allow the driver to relax and feel free to expose his weak points and discuss any aspects of his performance. His openness will encourage the engineers to do the same, thus creating a virtuous circle that will transform weaknesses into opportunities to improve. Having this type of atmosphere is the key to a successful team performance.

# KEY POINTS

- The second phase of the P-D-R® process concerns decisions. In the standard process, it receives an input from the perception phase, which provides the best information a driver can base his decision on.

- The decision-making process can be divided into four key areas: the analysis of the problem, the exploration of all available options, the choice of the best option and a final review of the decision.

- The first step, problem analysis, consists in cross-checking all the information available with the context and the goal. Careful preparation and psychological strength will raise the driver's awareness in a specific situation and help him construct a series of connections between a problem and all the actions that can be taken to deal with it.

- A driver's ability to explore all possible options can be improved by preparing for likely and unlikely scenarios. It's essential for him to develop a sense of the alternatives available, so as to prioritize accordingly.

- One of these options will be the final call. When it comes to making a decision, a driver needs to focus on the final goal and his team's values. Being able to master his emotions under so much pressure is a key skill to assess the best option on the table.

- The decision process should always end with a review and accountability phase, which is necessary if a driver wants to learn from his choices, whether they were successful or not.

# THE
# REACTION
# PHASE

Race start at the Austrian GP 2020.
Courtesy of F1-Fansite.com

YOU ONLY HAVE CONTROL OVER THE NEXT FEW MOMENTS, NOT THREE LAPS BACK OR TWO AHEAD, SO IT'S CRUCIAL TO FIND THAT ABSENCE OF THINKING THAT LETS YOU CONNECT AND FULLY ENGAGE WITH WHAT YOU ARE DOING – DRIVING FROM ONE CORNER TO THE NEXT AS BEST YOU CAN.

Driving a race car can be defined as the sum over time of numerous perceptions, decisions and reactions aimed at pursuing the final goal: being faster than your opponents. The third step of the P-D-R® model is the reaction phase, which is the last part of our driving process. When it's reaction time, the driver has to translate his ability into results, his perceptions into actions.

This is when pure driving skills become fundamental. At this point you may be thinking about steering control – changing direction with speed and accuracy – but I'm actually referring to every single action a driver performs to manage the car and enhance its performance.

Perception is the phase in which a driver understands and frames the situation he is experiencing, thanks to his natural ability and his meticulous preparation. Decision comes right after that, when the driver analyzes the information collected during the perception phase and chooses what to do next. In the standard process his final choice is the input for the reaction phase.

As we saw in the first chapter, there are two different ways of getting to the reaction phase:

- The **Standard** P-D-R® model
- The **Instinctive** P-D-R® model.

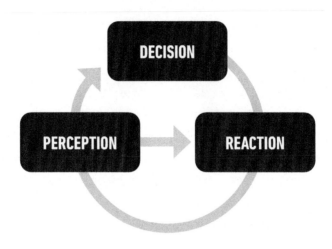

*Figure 4.1: Standard and instinctive P-D-R® models*

In both models the reaction phase executes an instruction that was produced beforehand, which suggests that the perception phase includes an area that directly produces instructions. These special inputs emerge from the driver's subconscious (rather than being the product of a rational decision) and go straight to the reaction domain, where they get translated into action.

Given this binary input option, we can identify two different reactions, associated to the specific nature of the two possible types of input – the ones produced by a rational decision and the ones that are related to the driver's subconscious:

1. **Calculated reactions** (Standard P-D-R®)

2. **Instinctive reactions** (Instinctive P-D-R®).

In the reaction phase there is a single goal: to complete the action determined by the chosen input. However, the two possible types of reaction are quite different from each other.

The first difference is related to the time needed for execution. Calculated reactions are employed in situations where the driver has time to go through the full process, which can be measured in seconds. We can set an arbitrary minimum threshold of 1 second, although we need to keep it flexible in view of the complexity of the process. Every reaction that takes longer than 1 second can be defined as calculated.

Conversely, instinctive reactions involve a much faster process, which can only be measured in tenths of a second. In this type of situation, the speed of every action is below our arbitrary 1-second threshold.

Since a highly professional athlete generally has a reaction time in the range of 100-500 milliseconds, the choice of a 1-second threshold serves the purpose of grouping everything that is influenced by the driver's reaction time under the umbrella of instinctive reactions.

The second difference between the two types of reaction is that the instinctive one usually involves a physical performance, which is why we talk about reaction time. This can be defined as the time elapsing between the beginning of the application of a stimulus and the beginning of our reaction to it.

The act of driving is a continuous sum of actions. If we represent calculated and instinctive reactions in a single chart, we can see an overlap of a low-frequency signal corresponding to calculated reactions with a high-frequency one representing the instinctive domain, as in Figure 4.2.

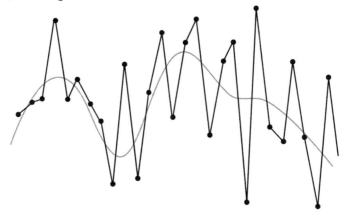

*Figure 4.2: Calculated and instinctive reactions*

In the P-D-R® model these two types of reaction exist at the same time. Following the principles of Signal Theory, we can say that **driving is the sum of a driver's infinite calculated and instinctive actions. The whole process is the combination of both types of reactions.** Let's imagine a situation in which a driver is trying to overtake the car in front, studying the moves of the other driver and his braking points, in order to understand where he can be faster and pull off a successful maneuver. A good setting for this scenario could be Spa-Francorchamps, one of the most amazing tracks in the world. Our driver might realize that he is faster in La Source (Turn 1) and through the Eau Rouge-Raidillon sector (Turns 3-4-5).

*Figure 4.3: The Spa-Francorchamps circuit map*

He knows that overtaking on the Kemmel straight, before getting to Les Combes, is his best shot, but he also knows that overtaking too soon on that straight means opening the possibility of being overtaken again when braking into Turn 7. Therefore he decides to go for a late pass on the Kemmel straight, so his opponent won't have enough room to overtake him back until they are out of Turn 16, through Blanchimont.

This calculated reaction comes at the end of a Standard P-D-R® process, which starts with the perception of the problem – understanding where he is faster and how the track layout can help him achieve his goal. Once the driver has a clear grasp of the situation, he is able to list and prioritize his options. Should he overtake on the Kemmel straight or out of Blanchimont? And if he chooses the Kemmel straight, should he do it in the first or second part, braking into Les Combes? He will use all the information and background knowledge that are available to him in order to make the best possible decision.

Let's not forget that in the meantime he is still driving, controlling the car, trying to stay in the wake of the car in front and edging closer to it, getting away from the curb, maybe saving an oversteer moment out of Turn 1 or delaying a downshift to avoid locking the rear tires. Clearly, all these instinctive reactions, which are a natural consequence of driving a car at the limit, can't be put on hold while the driver is preparing his move. **He is constantly receiving information through his own body, from visual and auditory cues and from the steering wheel. He reacts instinctively on the basis of his pure driving ability, experience and background knowledge, responding to all perceptions as fast as his reaction time allows him.**

## Calculated Reactions

When the process follows the standard path, the driver has time to make a conscious decision about the best course of action before putting it into practice.

Imagine what it's like to be overtaken when there are only three laps to go. You still have a shot at gaining your position back, but it's a very stressful situation, which involves a variety of emotions. Being overtaken puts you in a difficult position: you naturally feel anxious and maybe you worry about being judged by other people, but you also try to be positive and hope you can be fast enough to win back your previous position.

**Letting your emotions overwhelm you is a recipe for disaster, because it shifts your focus from the concentrated action of driving a race car to distracting factors that won't do anything for you but slow you down.**

For a calculated reaction to be successful, a professional driver needs to keep the following fundamental points in mind:

- Focus on the task
- Control emotions and anxiety
- Exclude all distractions.

A driver's priority should be achieving his goal. Pressure is always high when driving a race car and a driver needs to get used to this, because the pressure certainly won't decrease over the course of his career. If anything, it will increase, because when he's more experienced, more will be expected of him. The higher the series he is competing in, the higher the stakes will be. Moreover, public exposure is bound to create additional stress.

That's why it's essential for a driver to be mentally strong. Keeping your mind on the goal, controlling emotions and excluding distractions are the prerequisites of a good calculated reaction – clearly, mental toughness is a key element.

A good performance is the sum of what a driver can influence – i.e. the way he drives – and other elements that are necessarily out of his control, such as the equipment at his disposal, his competitors' performances and the weather. Therefore, a driver knows that he needs to be at his best to have a shot at winning. It all lies in his ability to focus on the moment, to the exclusion of everything that can distract him from his goal.

For instance, if he wants to gain back the position he has lost, his focus needs to be on driving as well as he can, hitting his marks to have a shot at overtaking his opponent. When you're overtaken, there is a real risk of getting stuck in that frustration and losing your focus because you keep on thinking about what happened. Obviously, that's not going to help you achieve your goal. When this happens, a good call from his engineer will help the driver find his focus again.

**You only have control over the next few moments, not three laps back or two ahead, so it's crucial to find that absence of thinking that lets you connect and fully engage with what you are doing – driving from one corner to the next as best you can.**

Emotions need to be kept out of your way or used to your advantage. Although several studies have shown that a reasonable level of anxiety can help sharpen your focus and get into the zone, there is a fine line between a stimulating level of anxiety and an excessive one. If you go over a certain threshold, it's difficult to keep your emotions under control and your performance is going to suffer.

More specifically, high levels of stress will tighten the driver's muscles, lower his attention level and shift the focus away from the present. As a consequence, his reaction time will get slower and his driving will be affected.

In addition to this, distracting elements will start creeping into the driver's mind and he will lose his confidence. He'll start questioning his own ability and his chances of success:

- Will I be fast enough?
- What are the others going to think?
- If I don't make it, will I lose this opportunity?

Once these questions enter his brain, he is likely to make mistakes. That's why he needs to learn to manage his emotions, either on his own or with the help of the people around him. In my experience, a simple word at the right time can totally turn things around. When one of my drivers is not performing well enough, I can tell from his voice over the radio if he is upset or not fully in the zone. When this happens, there is no point in going through a lot of data or asking him to do this and that. The best approach is to calm him down and make him focus on something that will give him the confidence to perform.

Drivers often make mistakes, like locking up, going off road or simply spinning the car around. It happens, and it's due to many factors. The problem is that when something like this occurs, they are very likely to lose confidence.

I think we are all familiar with this type of situation. Whatever job we do, if we get something wrong, our minds tend to go back to that moment again and again, with the risk of getting stuck in an endless loop. If we let this happen, we end up losing focus on the present and possibly making another mistake.

We need to remember that time flows only in one direction, so we should always focus on what we can control rather than something we can't change any more. A mistake is disruptive, but we need to move on in spite of it. When a driver blows a corner and loses his focus, it would certainly be counterproductive for his engineer to come on the radio with a negative comment – it would stress the driver even more. In a situation like this, the engineer's task is to help the driver stop thinking about that corner and regain his focus on the present moment. Dwelling on a mistake while you're still driving won't bring you any benefit. On the contrary, it is very likely to slow you down.

As we saw earlier in the book, it is important to go back and analyze what we did wrong, to make sure we won't repeat the same mistake, but the right time to do that is after the race, not while you're still driving.

## Instinctive Reactions

As spectators, we get really excited when we see a driver overtaking at the limit, having full control of the car while making a sharp turn or braking at the last moment. We all realize that going over the limit and getting away with it is a special achievement.

I must admit that when I see one of my drivers doing this type of maneuver, it always puts a smile on my face. It makes me proud not only of him but also of myself, because it means that together we have found the link between man and machine that can challenge all expectations. It's just magical.

**A driver has an infinitesimal amount of time to perceive the limits of the car and adjust his braking, steering and accelerating. He perceives the car with his body and his eyes, through the sounds he hears and the feel of the steering wheel. He is continuously adjusting to the variety of inputs he receives and dancing across the peak grip of the tires. The speed of his reactions needs to be fast enough to allow him to maintain control of the car with a minimum safety margin. Sometimes there is no margin at all.**

Qualifying is the time when drivers usually find that extra bit of time, pushing their cars to the limit and beyond. After qualifying I've often heard my drivers say that they didn't know it was possible to carry that sort of speed into the corner. This means that they just went for it, pushing the car beyond what they thought was actually achievable.

Let's not forget that we are talking about real racing, not online competitions. It requires real bravery to test the limits of your car when your own life is at risk.

The instinctive domain includes all those reactions that occur in a time that is comparable to a person's reaction time. Therefore I've set an upper threshold of one second, which is high compared to the reaction time of a professional athlete, but should just be considered as an upper limit. As we saw earlier in the chapter, driving is a continuous series of actions in response to a series of events, hence the reaction time is involved throughout the whole process.

There are many situations in which the driver's reaction time is vital for his performance, such as:

- The start of a race: milliseconds can lead to meters of difference when braking at the first corner

- Oversteer control

- Braking

- Switch change (there are situations in which a switch change needs to be done in a specific moment of the race)

- Throttle application

- Pit stops

- Restarting after a caution

- Dodging an obstacle in front of the car

- Getting out of the cockpit if there is an accident.

Of course, these are just a few examples – the list could be much longer. The point is that a good and consistent reaction time makes a driver fast and reliable and helps him get to the limit and beyond. In the P-D-R® process the instinctive reaction is introduced as a shortcut between the perception and reaction phases. The input that leads to an instinctive reaction is still an instruction that needs to be turned into action, but the nature of that command, which comes directly from the perception area, is slightly different from the input that leads to a calculated reaction.

**There is a part of the perception area that is linked to the driver's subconscious and issues instructions for fast responses over car control and command execution. This kind of perception gets fed by the driver's experience: all he has learned by driving cars and training his body to feel the movements of the car in response to his inputs throughout his career.**
In many ways, a high-profile driver is the most expensive and complex sensor that you can put in a car. That's why it's important to pay a lot of attention to what the driver has to say about the car's performance. Even if the data don't show any sign of a problem, an experienced driver will be able to perceive it, because he can instinctively feel that something differs from what he was expecting to perceive.

This awareness comes from comparing what he feels while driving with his internal database of experience, which is filled with years of driving perceptions. I've found myself in this situation a few times in my career, when I was trying to debug a problem that I couldn't see in the data, even if I had a vast amount of information in front of me. In these situations, the driver's perceptions were invaluable, because deep down in the driver's perception area there were some expectations related to his commands that were not matched by the car. The driver realized that his actions were leading to unexpected results in terms of car behavior and was able to give us some precious information: how the car should have responded to his inputs in comparison to how he felt it was actually reacting. It was only by investigating the differences he had pointed out that we managed to finally understand what the problem was.

It is sometimes difficult to properly explain how a car should behave – all the driver can say is something like "it just doesn't feel right". This means that he can't fully describe his perception. However, he would recognize that perception if he felt it again, which suggests that his body is able to store and catalog the perceptions it has collected over the years, as if it were a computer database.

The inputs that determine an instinctive reaction are instructions produced by a part of the perception area that contains all the driving experience a driver has accumulated, absorbed and perfected over his career.

There are many situations in which the instructions produced by the driver's subconscious produce an immediate, instinctive reaction. For example, in response to a wheel lock when braking or an oversteer moment, the driver cannot afford to make any conscious decisions but needs to take immediate action. This is when his reaction time – the interval between his perception of an event and the correction he applies, for example on the steering wheel or the brake pedal – comes into play.

Reaction time has become more and more the focus of attention for doctors following high-performing athletes, because it's widely recognized that an improved reaction time can give you a significant advantage over your opponent in all sports. Therefore, the teams of doctors and physiotherapists that assist drivers in their daily training, working on all physical aspects of their performance, use several methods to improve their reaction time.

Just to give you a broad idea of how physically demanding driving a race car can be, here is a list of parameters of normal conditions that are reached during a race:

- Longitudinal and lateral forces up to 5 G

- Vertical shock forces with peaks > 10 G

- Brake pedal force > 150 kgf

- Temperature in the cockpit: 40-80 degrees Celsius

- Steering torque: 9-16 Nm.

Driving a race car is definitely not a walk in the park!
It is part of a personal trainer's job to help drivers improve their reaction time, particularly in demanding physical and psychological conditions, in order to prepare them for what they are going to experience in the car. According to the literature on the subject as well as my own experience, the reaction time of an athlete, in our case a driver, should aim to be:

1. As fast as possible

2. As consistent as possible.

The first point is quite clear and doesn't need much explanation – obviously, the faster his reaction time is, the faster his response to a stimulus is going to be. This gives him an advantage over his opponents, helps to free up his mental capacity for his next task, and often makes the difference between losing control of the car and spinning in the gravel or bringing it back under control.

The second point is less intuitive and requires an explanation, since it indirectly suggests sacrificing pure performance for the sake of consistency. Let's consider for example a driver who has an average reaction time of 220 milliseconds at the best of his condition.

After one hour of driving, however, when his heart rate is high and he is dehydrated and tired, his reaction time will go up to 550 milliseconds. This suggests that his performance is going to suffer later in the race, which clearly isn't a desirable characteristic. This is especially true in endurance racing, in which there are multiple-hour stints, sometimes including driving at night, as in 24-hour races like Le Mans or the 24 Hours of Daytona or Spa.

The consistency of a driver's reaction time needs to become a training target, and should always be balanced with pure performance speed in order to find the best combination of these two parameters.

There are lots of techniques that are being used and have proven to be effective, such as light boards, disruptive glasses and so on. Nowadays this aspect of training is well covered by the physiotherapists and doctors specialized in enhancing athletes' performances.

All a driver needs to do is add these features to his training target list.

More specifically, a tool that has proven to work very well in improving reaction time is the simulator, which is used by all race car drivers but can also be very effective when training for other disciplines. We are going to examine its features and benefits in the next chapter.

Summing up, the reaction phase is a sum of calculated and instinctive reactions. As we have seen, both can be trained by working on different skills, with the common goal of improving the whole reaction process.

# KEY POINTS

- The third part of the P-D-R® process is the Reaction phase, in which the driver executes the decision he has taken, with or without the help of his team.

- There are two types of reactions: calculated and instinctive.

- Calculated reactions, which are based on the standard P-D-R® process, take place when the driver has enough time to consider all the options that are available to him. For a calculated reaction to be successful, a driver needs to focus on his task, control his emotions and exclude all distracting thoughts from his mind.

- Instinctive reactions define the instinctive P-D-R® process. They occur when the sequence of actions and events is so fast that there is no time for a standard process. The driver cannot evaluate all the options available and needs to react without making a conscious choice. In this case the input for his reaction comes from a separate area of the perception phase, corresponding to the driver's subconscious perceptions. A great deal of practice, mental toughness and experience are vital prerequisites for successful instinctive reactions.

# THE ROLE OF SIMULATORS

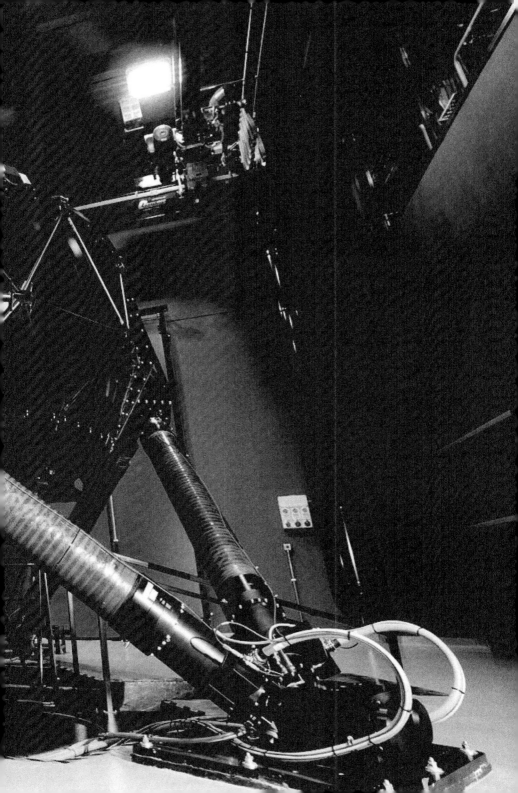

SIMULATOR DEVELOPERS ARE ABLE TO MODEL ALMOST ANYTHING, WHICH OPENS UP ENDLESS POSSIBILITIES AND – COMBINED WITH THE POTENTIAL FOR CLEAN BACK-TO-BACK COMPARISONS – ENABLES DRIVERS TO NOTICE DIFFERENCES THAT THEY WOULDN'T BE ABLE TO APPRECIATE WHEN DRIVING A REAL CAR.

Each of the areas we have looked at so far can be the focus of attention during training sessions: drivers can develop these skills separately, knowing that this will enhance their whole performance. However, **training specific skills will allow drivers to improve only up to a certain point. Ultimately, it's essential to combine everything together through the most complete exercise a driver can perform: driving.**

This is common to all sports, of course. If you think about tennis, for example, you can practice your service, forehand and backhand from all parts of the court, along with your volleys, overheads and drop shots. You can also work on your physical and psychological condition, since much of your performance will depend on mental focus and stress management. At some point, though, you will need to put all these elements together by playing matches against other people, your team mates or your coach. That's the only way in which you can test all your skills at the same time and see what you have improved and what needs more work. Only a match can give you a clear picture of your strengths, weaknesses and overall progress.

The same happens in motorsport. A driver will benefit from dedicated trainings, event briefings, physical and psychological preparation, reaction time training and so on. However, at some point he needs to actually drive in order to bring it all together.

If he wants to do it in a real car, this may be complicated, depending on which series he is preparing for. In recent years Formula 1 has cut tests to save money, and the other top racing series have followed suit, because keeping costs under control is a priority nowadays. Seat time is extremely rare – and when it is available, it is very expensive.

On the other hand, Sports Car is a category that allows drivers to practice a lot, mainly because the cars need to be tested for endurance races. It's not unusual for teams preparing for the classic French 24-hour marathon or the 24 Hours of Daytona to run multiple endurance tests, involving 30 or more hours of consecutive driving, ahead of the competition.

NASCAR used to have several tire testing days. Although they have now been reduced, there is still a significant amount of track time that can be exploited. IndyCar has adopted a similar approach: the test days have been reduced in order for the teams to save on costs. If we look at other motorsport series, we can see that they have all limited real-track testing to reduce costs.

Since the number of training days has been drastically reduced, drivers, including those in top racing series, often end up spending days on their karts or on dirt track and late model cars. This type of training can help them prepare for driving high-spec race cars, so if they see a benefit, they will go for it.

**In view of the current situation, in which drivers have limited opportunities to practice their driving skills, simulators have become a very valuable tool for car and driver development. They are a very effective answer to a real need for an alternative way of training the whole set of skills required during a race.** The use of simulators is now very common for all drivers, starting from the big Formula 1 teams down to smaller teams competing in lower series.

There are so many models of simulators available on the market that we need to distinguish between two main kinds of tools:

- Professional driver in the loop / Hardware in the loop simulators

- High-spec home driving simulators.

The first ones are the multi-million-dollar hardware that top-level motorsport teams buy and develop. They are platforms with incredible engineering specs, including large and powerful cueing motion systems. Real car parts can be in the loop as well, so you can use and test an actual piece of hardware rather than a very complex multi-physical model.

The vehicle model in this first category is custom-made, hence it offers almost infinite possibilities of improvement and complexity. These models are usually developed by teams of highly skilled engineers and represent the state of the art of modern automotive simulation.

In these simulators, the layout of the race tracks is mostly laser-scan based, using the latest data set available, and the graphics are constantly updated to be as realistic as possible. On the motion platform, the driver's office – i.e. the cockpit – is replicated with maximum fidelity, and so are the sounds and the visuals.

The second category, high-spec home simulators, has been gaining popularity in recent years. These tools, developed by software houses, are essentially high-spec gaming platforms based on excellent car and race tracks models.

These simulators offer drivers the possibility of home training. Although they are less accurate and realistic than the ones they can use in the factory headquarters, they are still a very valuable tool for their goals. In addition to very good direct drive steering wheels and load cell-based brake pedals, sometimes they are also endowed with small motion systems to offer some sort of cueing.

## How to Approach a Simulator

I have been lucky enough to work with several high-performance simulators – as a user, as a performance engineer, as a developer and as a vehicle dynamicist. Having been involved in sessions with many racing categories and drivers (from Formula 1 to LMP1, NASCAR, IndyCar, GP2 (now F2), GP3 (now F3), F4, Indy Lights and Super Formula), over the years I have realized that drivers tend to approach simulators in one of two ways:

- As if it were a real car
- As a model of a real car.

The difference between these two approaches is subtle but fundamental, because it will determine whether a session is successful or not.

If a driver expects the simulator to feel like a real car, he is bound to be disappointed. As soon as he gets into the simulator, he will start complaining that it's nothing like reality, so he can't drive it. Throughout the session, no matter how useful it can be to him or his team, he will keep repeating that it doesn't feel like a real car.

On the other hand, there are drivers who approach the simulator knowing full well that what they are about to drive is the best model that their team has been able to produce, trying to replicate their race car as much as possible. During their session, they may rightly point out that it feels different from a real car, but this will not stop them from getting the best out of the session. Moreover, their expert comments will contribute to the constant improvement of the tool. In my experience, the drivers who adopt this more positive approach always manage to learn something useful from the use of the simulator, while also helping their team.

Race drivers usually spend a day or two at the team's headquarters in order to train with the simulator, work with the team, prepare the next race event or work on an upgrade of their car. It is important to remember that the simulator gives them the opportunity to learn and train using the closest replica of their race cars that is available on the market.

**Professionals simulators help drivers widen their perception area, including information that they wouldn't be able to pick up on the track. Simulator developers are able to model almost anything, which opens up endless possibilities and – combined**

**with the potential for clean back-to-back comparisons – enables drivers to notice differences that they wouldn't be able to appreciate when driving a real car.**

Let's consider an aerodynamic feature test, for example. If we tried to do it on the track, it would never be possible to have a clean back-to-back comparison, because there are always too many variables – such as wind, track temperature, tire temperature or traffic – that have an impact on the results of the test. This is just one of many possible examples: the same applies to engine mappings, hybrid system changes, mechanical setup changes, tire thermal conditions and so on.

What makes the simulation world incredibly powerful is the fact that the driver operates in a controlled environment. This means that in a comparison between two options, the different feedback from the platform and the other cues will be related only to the different parameters that have been loaded in the simulator. **What can be more useful than feedback from an extremely accurate car model, through a state-of-the-art platform and cueing system, which is isolated from all the interference you would certainly have on the track?**

Of course, I am not saying that simulators can or should replace real on-track testing – the experience they provide is clearly different. However, given today's limited resources and reduced test days, they are an extremely useful tool for drivers, because they give them the best opportunity to test the whole set of skills they have been training separately.

## Motion Platform Cues: The Driver's Perception

Many professional simulators have motion systems that try to replicate some of the cues of a real race car, with the ultimate goal of making the experience as realistic as possible for the driver.

There are several types of platform on the market: hexapod platforms, platforms on rails, platforms that can spin 360 degrees to replicate the car's yaw angle with great accuracy and so on. As you can imagine, costs escalate very quickly with these pieces of advanced engineering. However, teams and research labs are willing to spend a great deal of money on this because experience shows that if drivers receive realistic cues from the platform, they will drive the car model much more realistically. Clearly, this will result in a better simulation.

The development of motion systems requires extremely complex calculations, involving not only the mechanics but also the psychological and physical aspects of driving.

The sensitivity of the human body to displacement, velocity, acceleration and the variation of acceleration (also called jerk or jolt) is the subject of many studies. Jerk and acceleration are the dominant perceptions that our body is going to feel in the simulator. The motion of the platform can be optimized in many different ways, prioritizing some degrees of movement over others and fine-tuning different options.

On the basis of research and experience, we can state the following regarding platform motion:

- The primary focus is yaw motion, as the control of the car model depends on this feedback.

- Vertical motion is of secondary importance, but it matters for curb riding to be felt.

- Longitudinal and lateral motion is also secondary; given the limited space and actuator stroke available, it is always going to be compromised.

- Pitch and roll can be considered the least important cues; since formula race cars usually have limited travel in pitch and roll, the platform is able to replicate the real movement and accelerations, also considering their high-frequency content.

Here is an interesting issue I have often wondered about: if I could accurately replicate the real pitch and roll, what effect would it have in combination with the scaled-down motion feedback in the other degrees of freedom? I suppose that the driver's perception would be off – he would perceive those two movements to be unbalanced compared to the rest of the cues.

It's a trade-off in the end: since we are not able to replicate exactly what a real car does (because of the limits to the actuator stroke), one approach is to scale the pitch and roll down to make them con-sistent with the other degrees of freedom.

This is just an example of a possible compromise over motion settings. The list of choices and trade-offs could be long, including different approaches for road courses and ovals, as well as for tracks of different lengths – a quarter of a mile, half a mile, a mile and superspeedway tracks will require specific settings.

As previously mentioned, **drivers need to be aware that when they are in a simulator, they are not driving a race car but the best car model with the most advanced motion settings their team could provide them with. If they are aware of that and start the simulator session with the right approach, the experience will be much more productive for them and their team.**

The correlation of the car model with the real car is something that the team works on methodically and scientifically, using the best available data. As for the motion system, a good part of the correlation can be data based, but at some point it is always going to be dependent on the driver's feedback.

The driver has the opportunity to tailor the cueing settings to his perceptions in a cueing assessment session, in which, starting from the best current solution, a gradual and iterative process allows the team to improve the cues. The driver's feedback is very important in this process, because the goal is to adapt the motion to his needs, so he can feel the car and drive realistically. **When he gets to the point where he can drive consistently, close to the limits of the vehicle model, and is able to pick up the setup changes, it's time to end the cueing assessment and start the real session.**

In my experience, it's always worth spending a few hours with a new race driver while he's getting acquainted with the platform, to make sure he feels comfortable with the car model and can perceive the setup changes. During this process, it's a good idea to try a few simple changes in the mechanical balance, brake balance and aerodynamic balance. This will enable the driver to compare what he feels in the simulator with a feeling he is already familiar with, so he can evaluate if the cueing settings are right as they are or need to be adjusted. It's an iterative process that requires some patience.

Even when a driver has already used the platform, it is advisable to start his session with a cueing assessment. This is because our body tends to adapt, so a driver could perceive things differently in two different sessions, even though he is driving the same car model with the same setup and track. At the start of a new session it is good practice to do a baseline check to make sure that everything is ok and to flag any cueing issues compared to the previous time. The baseline can then be changed and become the new baseline for the next sessions.

There are two reasons for a driver to look forward to a cueing assessment session:

**1.** It gives him time to get acquainted with the platform and feel the differences between alternative cueing settings.

**2.** It helps him identify the cues that have a greater impact on how he feels the car model and on his ability to drive it at the limit.

The choice of cueing settings that drivers make is often unpredictable, because they all have different sensibilities. I have always been surprised by the fact that two different guys driving the same simulator, the same car model on the same track, end up choosing different settings. That's why, in my opinion, a driver needs to have his own cueing settings – he might have different perceptions from another individual, and this is enough to justify this approach. Not everybody would agree with me, though, and I've had many discussions with colleagues in the business over this. Others support a general motion approach, in which the settings are calculated through general data correlation and consequently are the same for all drivers. Although I believe that a data-correlated approach is a great starting point, there is something that it's just not possible to measure – the driver's perception of the motion platform.

The last point to consider in this respect is the effect of motion platforms on the simulation results. This topic is very controversial and it's difficult to give a definitive answer. The main point is that the cues from a motion system will never be the same as those from a real car, because of inherent power and space constraints. There is always the possibility that the platform may malfunction and produce the wrong cues.

Considering this, you may wonder if it's worth spending millions on complicated platforms to replicate the scaled cues of a car, knowing that it will never be the real deal. However, experience tells us that if we compare a driver's performance with and without active motion, the results will be quite different.

**A driver is likely to perform better when using a motion platform, as long as the motions make sense to him. Research and experience have highlighted the correlation of a driver's inputs to platform cues, showing a positive impact on the simulation performance.**

The point is that, even if a motion platform can't replicate the real car, drivers can still benefit from platform cues generated through sophisticated motion algorithms – the cues will make his driving experience more realistic, which will lead him to generate more significant inputs.

With some drivers, unfortunately, we need to accept that the motion settings won't help. In these cases, the best option is a static platform, since no cues are better than bad cues.

## Steering, Pedals and Other Simulator Cues

The cues provided by motion platforms are not the only important cues in the simulator: there are others, known as "the fundamentals", that are even more significant:

- Visual cues
- Sound cues
- Steering wheel feedback
- Pedal feedback.

These are the fundamental features that dynamic and static simulators have in common.

High-resolution projectors and finely detailed graphic models are standard features in professional simulators. The track models are always updated to keep up with updates to the real track: both the graphic model and the physical part of the track are usually reworked when the real race track is refurbished.

This service is provided by some well-known companies in the online gaming world, like iRacing, AssettoCorsa and Codemaster. Even some top motorsport series teams, including Formula 1 teams, use their commercial track models, which are also available to the general public, for their simulators.

Sophisticated and expensive audio systems replicate a wide range of realistic sounds, such as wheels locking, rolling over curbs or grass, different engine sounds, electric motors and so on. In professional simulators we can also find additional cues, like gear beeps or understeer beeps through the radio, as well as other artificial cues that can be helpful to the driver.

Sound and visual cues are crucial for good simulation results. If the graphic model is not accurate or a brake marker is ten meters away from where it should be, it won't take long for drivers to notice that their marks are wrong. I'll give you an example from my own experience. A few years ago, I was working on the Texas Speedway correlation for a NASCAR team. At the time, this 1.5-mile oval had some big bumps going into turns three and four. Nowadays the track has been resurfaced to smooth it out, but back then it was quite a ride landing there with a race car.

My simulator driver at the time, Bobby Labonte, a former Winston Cup champion, noticed that in the simulator the bumps came out of the blue, while in real life he was able to see them beforehand because of the reflection of the sunlight on the asphalt. I had great respect for him, but to be honest, when he said that I thought he was just being difficult!

However, it didn't take me long to realize that he was right to point that out – and besides, the same feedback was given later by another driver. So we decided to program the color of the graphics as a function of the road normals and the sunlight angle. When Bobby tried the new track model, he felt immediately, right from the first lap, that it was a major improvement in simulation realism. This is only one of the many things you can learn while working with a great, detail-oriented driver like Bobby. I will always be grateful for all I have learned from him.

Steering and pedals are essential cues for a driver. The pedals – i.e., the brake and the accelerator – need to replicate the feel of the real ones as much as possible. The throttle is usually linked to a potentiometer that measures pedal displacement, which is used as input to the simulation model. Most throttle installations have a damper connected to it and it's not uncommon to find the same part that is used in the car. The brake pedal is slightly more complex. The oil line doesn't really activate the calipers, unless there is a Hardware-In-the-Loop (HIL) installation. There is a pressure sensor that reads the driver's input and passes it to the vehicle model.

The principle on which the brake pedal input is based in all professional simulators and the most serious home installations is pressure rather than displacement. The aim is to have a feeling that is similar to that of a car – both travel and force. In a HIL brake system, the line has a different length from a real car. We are not really moving caliper pistons, and if we were, the discs would not be hot and rotating.

In short, it's a compromise and the brake pedal won't feel exactly as it would in a real car. Moreover, the lack of longitudinal deceleration doesn't help the driver push the brake: he is going to perceive the effort to reach peak pressure as greater than in a real car, because of the missing inertial effect of his weight onto the pedal.

The feel of the brake pedal can be tuned both in travel and force feedback. The goal is to be able to modulate the brake to control wheel locking, and at the same time have a decent feedback that feels like a real car.

Finally, the steering feedback is of crucial importance, because it enables the driver to feel what the car model is doing and to react. Professional simulators and home simulators can both use direct drive steering hardware, in which the electric motor that provides the feedback acts on the steering axis, offering higher precision and better response over high-frequency feedbacks.

These steering motors have few parameters to play with, from scaling torque to friction and damping, and with some tuning you can achieve a great steering feedback. Through the steering wheel the driver feels what the vehicle model produces as a steering torque, hence a professional simulator will inevitably have a better simulation result than a commercial one. The tire model and the car model are much more refined in a professional simulator, so the results produced end up being significantly more realistic.

The level of accuracy that can be reached in the steering is very high. Some drivers rely on it so much that the time invested in improving this cue is fully justified.

## The Simulator as a Training Tool

When we talk about training, the first thing that comes to mind is running or lifting weights, but for a race driver this is only a small part of his training program. As previously mentioned, drivers don't have many opportunities to train with a real car nowadays, so the simulator has become one of the most complete toys a driver can play with. However, some people think that only a rookie driver can benefit from using a simulator, whereas an experienced driver doesn't need this kind of training. Is this true? Let's explore this issue.

### Non-Professional Simulators
Let's start from non-professional simulators, the ones that almost all drivers – as well as many driving enthusiasts – have at home.

They have become a very popular tool, especially lately, when many people have been stuck at home because of the COVID-19 pandemic. Nowadays it's not uncommon to see drivers, other athletes and celebrities competing in e-sports.

This type of simulator could be considered just an expensive videogame, but for a driver it represents the opportunity to work on his skills. Simulator sessions offer plenty of benefits in terms of training and preparation, such as:

1. Becoming familiar with the track layout will help a driver get into the rhythm more quickly, when it's time to drive the real car.

2. He will be able to drive on a track that has been resurfaced and rescanned ahead of the race weekend.

3. He can work on his consistency and his marks.

4. Monitoring his own improvements over time and looking at the data will improve his self-assessment skills.

5. He can practice his instinctive reactions, even with the limited cues of a static simulator.

6. Racing with other drivers in online gaming will expose him to competition, giving him an opportunity to work on his psychological skills and review his decision-making process.

The list could be longer, but I believe that these benefits are enough to make my point. It's also worth mentioning that the new generation of drivers – including Formula 1, NASCAR, IndyCar and Sports Car drivers – are used to racing online.

**This is a trend we can't ignore. Let's not forget that drivers are very competitive people: they need competition as much as they need training, so if they realize that there are advantages in training with home simulators, they will certainly go for it.**

The new generation of drivers – the young guns in Formula 1, for example, like Leclerc, Verstappen, Norris, Gasly, Schumacher, Mazepin, Tsunoda and Ocon – all grew up with these tools at home, differently from the previous generation. In the early 2000s (not so long ago), the drivers who wanted to drive a simulator had to go to the factory headquarters, if they were lucky enough to drive for a team that had one. Nowadays, instead, growing up with the opportunity to drive a simulator every day – trying different tracks, racing online and looking at data – has massively increased the number of hours that new drivers spend in training.

A simple calculation will make this clearer: if a 10-year-old kid starts to use a home simulator for 3 hours a day, 70% of the year for 10 years, he will have accumulated 7,665 hours of driving by the time he is 20. Considering that the maximum length of a Formula 1 Grand Prix is 2 hours, it means that he has already completed almost 3,833 races. This is particularly impressive if you think that a driver who has had a great career of more than 10 years in Formula 1 will probably have no more than 250 races under his belt!

**It's easy to realize that the development of a young and talented aspiring driver will be helped and speeded up by the opportunity to use a home simulator. Of course, driving a real car is**

**different, but this tool is going to prepare a driver to adapt and learn more quickly in real life.**

This is related to another phenomenon – the rise of young motor-sport stars. The youngest drivers racing in Formula 1, NASCAR, IndyCar and other racing categories can all be seen playing on on-line platforms. Clearly this is a marketing opportunity and sponsors are generally involved, but these young people are very skilled and clearly love what they are doing.

Managing an online race is much more complicated than it looks: a driver needs to keep an eye on his car's parameters, think of his strategy, deal with other competitors and of course keep driving. The whole strategy is tuneable, the car setup can be modified, some of the car control parameters (like brake balance and differential) can be changed, the fuel needs to be managed, and so on, depending on the software being used. When a driver races online, he needs to see the bigger picture and have a wider understanding of what is going on – it's not enough to just drive. This kind of training is very useful indeed, because it prepares him to the multi-tasking requirements of driving a race car, especially with the level of technology employed in the top series.

### Professional Simulators

Let's now consider professional simulators with proper motion systems, a team of engineers behind their development and correlation, and a dedicated development driver doing most of the dirty work for the race driver.

The number of hours of work and the know-how behind these tools can be difficult to imagine even for the engineers that work in the business. Thanks to development teams, car models can have an infinite number of features. Every aspect of a model is developed to an incredibly high level, the cockpit is usually the real one and the session is structured as a proper test day. When a driver arrives for his session, he climbs into the platform, gets strapped to his seat and starts driving.

There are two kinds of activity we can perform when a race driver is in the simulator:

**1.** Car development

**2.** Race preparation.

It's important for the driver to know the goal of a session in advance, because the two options require quite different states of mind. In a car development session, the team will have prepared different design options or concepts for the driver to experience. This kind of session can be stressful, because if the team wants a driver to test a few options, it goes without saying that they expect to discard some of them. Therefore some of the options tested will be good, while others will necessarily be less good.

In this kind of exercise, **a driver will use his perception skills to provide feedback that can be useful for the engineers to further develop the options tested or the simulator itself. After all, the simulator is the most advanced simulation tool available to the team, especially when coupled with a driver in the loop.**

I am aware that, from a driver's point of view, this type of session can be boring and stressful. However, if we consider that there are people that work overtime and sacrifice time with their family and friends to make him go faster in the real car, I would say that having a positive and proactive attitude when testing different options in a simulator is the least a driver can do.

If a driver points the engineers in the right direction, his contribution will eventually make him faster, because the team will learn from his feedback and develop that concept. Even a negative result can lead to a positive outcome for the driver, since it will prevent a bad solution from being implemented in the real car. Ultimately, it will save him from a worse performance when lap time really count.

Clearly, drivers can derive a more immediate benefit from the second type of session, aimed at preparing for a race. These sessions give drivers the opportunity to test many setup directions in a controlled environment, which helps them choose the optimal car settings and setup direction ahead of the actual race.

Although there is an endless list of options one can test in a simulator, the engineers generally pre-select the features they believe to be more crucial for optimizing a driver's performance.

The whole simulator experience is a form of training, because it has the same rhythm as a day at the track:

- Day briefing and run plan

- AM session
- Lunch break
- PM session
- Driver's debrief

Scheduling a session just like a track day helps the driver to concentrate better and feel more involved. There is a real risk of a drop in the driver's attention level during simulator sessions, so the team needs to do everything possible to stop this from happening.

I have seen sessions in which a driver was asked to do 160 laps per day, for 3 days in a row. This would be a high number even in a race car, where you have the adrenaline helping you stay focused. You can imagine how much harder it is to concentrate for such a long period of time in a simulator – the quality of the results is bound to suffer under these circumstances.

When going through the run plan with the engineers, it is always good practice to discuss some general points like:

- Number of laps during the day
- Run length to stabilize lap time
- Scheduled breaks
- Number of test items per day and test procedures.

Simulator sessions will induce the driver to use and train the three areas of the P-D-R® process. He will be able to feel the difference between alternative setup options, perceive each one and understand the problems and compromises each solution involves. This exercise will hit all the main points of the perception area, increasing the driver's awareness of car behavior and performance sensitivity for that specific track.

The driver's perception of the different options will lead him and the engineers to decide which ones to retain in the baseline setup. This gives him the opportunity to practice his decision-making skills, by evaluating the options available and making a well-considered choice. He will also be able to review his decision, compare it with the data and discuss it with the engineers.

The decision area will also be trained by working on different driving styles, possibly in a race simulation, and trying to manage tire wear in different ways based on the feeling he is getting through the simulator. In doing so, the driver will train his calculated reaction skills.

On the other hand, reacting to the main limitations of the vehicle model will help him train his instinctive reaction skills, so as to be more prepared for when he's going to put the wheels on the real asphalt.

Another important part of a professional driving simulator is the cockpit mock-up that is bolted to the platform. To make sure that the whole simulation is a full immersion in the driver's usual operating conditions, it replicates the driver's cockpit in the real car. This means that it includes all the options and commands available in the car and allows the driver to make any switch change during the session.

It's no secret that during the season Formula 1 teams organize a few sessions with the drivers they are going to put in the cars. In these sessions, drivers test procedures, perform starts, try to manage emergency maneuvers like a puncture or an engine failure, switch-on or switch-off procedures, and so on.

To give you an example, when I was working with the LMP1-H, we used to introduce fake car faults in the simulator to train both drivers and engineers to non-standard procedures. They had to try to manage the fault, fix it or decide the best thing to do.

**This kind of training is priceless both for rookies and for experienced drivers. Although 99% of the time they won't need to face such complex situations, being prepared for that 1% probability will make the difference between finishing the race and parking the car on the grass.**

This is one of the most complete ways in which a driver can train, second only to the actual test on track. Given the vast number of possible scenarios we can recreate in a simulator, this tool has a crucial role to play in a driver's training and development.

# KEY POINTS

- Professional driving simulators offer a series of options – including motion platforms – that are not available in the most common home simulators. One of the main differences is the complexity and correlation behind the car model, which is developed to be the best possible representation of the real car. The combination of this and the motion cues offered by the platform and the motion system helps to create a driving experience that is as close as possible to driving a real car. This enables drivers to go through car development and race preparation programs with their engineering teams. A training day in a professional simulator is scheduled like a track day, which helps with focus and mental engagement. It's a great training opportunity for drivers.

- One of the main advantages of professional driving simulators is that they offer the opportunity to test countless procedures and setups. The high complexity of the car models, the motion platform, and the replica of the real cockpit and steering layout make them a source of invaluable information and a prime training ground for drivers, who can use them to train each area of the P-D-R® process.

- Home simulators have become more and more important in drivers' daily lives. They are based on simpler car models and involve only the fundamental cues, without a motion platform. They are very useful to drivers because they enable them to train at home, combining all the skills they have been training separately. They can speed up a driver's development, giving him the opportunity to get used to multitasking driving processes, measure himself continuously against others in online racing and train each area of the P-D-R® process. In the meantime, his psychological skills are stimulated by the stress and complexity of simulation challenges and competitions.

The Rettifilo Chicane, Monza 2020.
Courtesy of F1-Fansite.com

THE MOST WINNING
STRATEGY IS TO FOCUS ON
YOUR PERFORMANCE RATHER
THAN THE RESULT ITSELF.
IF YOU MANAGE TO ENHANCE
YOUR SKILLS, WINNING
IS SIMPLY GOING TO BE
THE DIRECT CONSEQUENCE
OF YOUR OPTIMIZED
PERFORMANCE.

# CONCLUSION

We have come to the end of this book and it's time to take stock. In the previous chapters we explored the different phases of the P-D-R® process, breaking each part down into different areas in order to understand which factors contribute to improving a driver's performance.

First of all, we saw that raising a driver's awareness of the car performance envelope and preparing him for all kinds of extreme situations will help to enhance his perception. We then focused on the importance of a driver's psychological condition – which has a major impact on his performance – and associated the P-D-R® concept with the skills described in the Performance Pyramid.

We also looked at the area of the perception block that stores all the information collected by the driver over his career, which allows him to react instinctively and control the car without any conscious decisions.

We stressed the importance of decision-making skills and described the process by which a driver can make the best possible choice by analyzing his perceptions and exploring all the options available. The role of the subsequent decision review process was also emphasized.

When considering the reaction phase, we saw that a driver can have two different types of reaction, calculated and instinctive ones, depending on the situation he is facing.

Finally, the last chapter focused on the role of driving simulators. These sophisticated tools have become an essential part of a driver's training, especially in view of the fact that real track testing has been drastically reduced in recent years. As we remarked, both professional and non-professional simulators offer drivers an invaluable opportunity to train all their driving skills at the same time.

As you may have noticed, all the areas examined point to the crucial role played by training and preparation. The PDR® process provides a simple but effective framework for training each individual skill and optimizing your overall performance. After all, **the most winning strategy is to focus on your performance rather than the result itself. If you manage to enhance your skills, winning is simply going to be the direct consequence of your optimized performance.**

# REFERENCES

Hanson, B. Sport Coaching Styles: The Four DISC Styles. (n.d.). https://athleteassessments.com/four-sport-coaching-styles.

Kaya, A. (2014). Decision Making by Coaches and Athletes in Sport. *Procedia - Social and Behavioral Sciences* 152: 333-338.

Leysk, J. J. (1998). The Nine Mental Skills of Successful Athletes. *Ohio Center for Sport Psychology.* https://www.sportpsych.org/nine-mental-skills-overview.

Purcell, R., Gwyther, K. & Rice, S.M. (2019, November 28). Mental Health in Elite Athletes: Increased Awareness Requires an Early Intervention Framework to Respond to Athlete Needs. *Sports Med - Open* 5, 46. https://doi.org/10.1186/s40798-019-0220-1.

Rendon-Velez, E., Leeuwen, P., Happee, R., Horvath, I., van der Vegte, W., & de Winter, J. (2016, July 13). The Effects of Time Pressure on Driver Performance and Physiological Activity: A Driving Simulator Study. *Transportation Research Part F: Traffic Psychology and Behaviour*, Volume 41, Part A:150-169. https://doi.org/10.1016/j.trf.2016.06.013.

# ACKNOWLEDGMENTS

Life is full of surprises. Months ago I started writing mostly for myself, to collect all the lessons I have learned over the years as a sort of roadmap to follow in my daily work, a guideline for my mind. I certainly didn't expect my notes to turn into a book.

The first and biggest thank you goes to my wife, Arianna, who has always supported me and believed in me over many racing seasons around the world. It takes two to tango and she has always been there for me. Thanks for helping me be the man I am today, I'm proud to be by your side, Ari!

In my life I've had the privilege of working with many drivers and I really should thank each one of them for what I've been able to learn. One of them is Romain Grosjean, a driver and a friend: I owe him a huge thank you for all the time spent together around the world and for writing the nicest foreword I could ask for! He was always able to put a smile on my face when driving one of my cars, often doing something I didn't believe could be possible – merci beaucoup, mon ami!

Inspiration comes in unexpected ways. I learned this a long time ago, when I had the pleasure of working with Bobby Labonte, former NASCAR Champion. His story, his personality and his attitude really opened my eyes and boosted my passion for this job. I will always be grateful for the time we spent working together!

I also want to thank Guenther Steiner for allowing me to work on this project. His support has been very important for me to find the right state of mind to complete the job. In a Formula 1 season including more than twenty races, it is not easy to find the time to work on a book, but having your boss's support definitely gives you a great push!

Another thank you goes to Professor Massimo Guiggiani, who taught me a great deal about Vehicle Dynamics and was able to inspire me and help me develop my passion. I'm sure I speak for the many students who have had the privilege of participating in his lessons when I say "Grazie Prof!".

A special thank you to my publisher Denise Cumella, my writing consultant Elisabetta Zancan and all the people at Libri D'Impresa for turning my ideas into this book!

A big thank you to my friends and colleagues that went through the first version of this book: Sam Lishak, Richard Davis, Andrea Quintarelli and Carlo Pasetti, your feedback meant a lot to me!

Last but not least, a heartfelt thank you to my family for their constant love and support, and a special one to my parents, Rosa and Ermanno, for always showing me the way!

Ernesto Desiderio.
Ph. by Andy Hone

# THANK YOU FOR READING UP TO HERE!

I hope I have helped you understand how a driver can optimize his performance by following an effective method. I want to thank you for choosing me as a traveling companion for this journey in the world of car racing.

I'd love to know your opinion of this book.
Has it been useful to you? Which part have you found more interesting?
Please write your review on Amazon and let me know what you think.
It would really mean a lot to me.

Keep on following me on my social media accounts: you will be constantly updated on everything that concerns my work.
If you want to get in touch with me, please visit my LinkedIn Profile or send an email to e.desiderio@hotmail.it.

Printed in Great Britain
by Amazon